BRITISH MEN OF SCIENCE

General Editor
Sir Gavin de Beer F.R.S., F.S.A.

membre correspondant de l'Institut de France

Joseph Priestley

Joseph Priestley

REVOLUTIONS OF
THE EIGHTEENTH CENTURY

F. W. GIBBS
D.SC., PH.D., F.R.I.C.

Doubleday & Company, Inc.
Garden City, New York
1967

Contents

List of Plates

List of Figures

Preface

ANYONE who tries to portray the life and work of that great Englishman, Joseph Priestley, will be embarrassed by the sheer wealth of information about him, in both manuscript and printed sources. It will be necessary to select, and the broader the canvas the more difficult will the choice become. Since Priestley's activities touched almost all aspects of life in the eighteenth century, his biographer may well be appalled at the extent of the task and of his own ignorance ; for no one can claim to be familiar with developments in every field at any one period of history. He must, nevertheless, try to get to grips with it all, if only to ensure that his own special interests do not give a false cast to the features of his subject.

That is what I have tried to do in this book, sketching the broad outline and leaving the details for the more curious to fill in. Priestley's life, and his scientific work, can be divided into fairly distinct periods, and this has made it possible to deal with most of his research in six separate chapters (3, 5, 6, 8, 9, and 11). The rest of the book forms a continuous story in itself. It is hoped that this treatment will help the general reader to follow the biographical portion more easily, and the student to relate the scientific chapters to the various episodes in Priestley's life and the general contemporary background. I am grateful to the Editor for encouraging me to make some departure from the general plan of the series, and to the publishers for allowing me more than the normal amount of space for the purpose.

Though the work has been carried out single-handed, I owe much to those who have helped in the quest for information: to Professor Douglas McKie, mentor and friend, through whom I first learnt the value of studies of this kind; to Dr

W. A. Smeaton, whose knowledge of French history has been a great help and who has done me numerous services; to those who have given time to discuss certain aspects of the work, and particularly the Rev. Roger Thomas of Dr Williams's Library; and to many other librarians who have given valued assistance, some with straws and others with whole bricks. Priestley was greatly pleased when the travelling time between Birmingham and London was reduced from 48 to 24 hours, and I similarly benefited from the opening of the M1, which made it possible for me to visit the Central Reference Library and the Assay Master's Office in Birmingham, and the Warwickshire Records Office, to more effect than would otherwise have been possible. The Council of the Royal Society kindly allowed me to consult and use their records freely.

It is also a pleasure to record the courtesy and help that I have received from several individuals and societies in America to whom my inquiries led. Finally, I wish to thank especially a few correspondents who, since this book was announced, have taken the trouble to inform me of pieces of information that have come their way. I hope they will not now be disappointed.

F. W. GIBBS

Northwood
July 1963

Chapter 1

Early Promise

TODAY it is rare for a man, especially a scientist, to become famous in more than one field at once. Joseph Priestley (1733–1804), on the other hand, preferred to think of himself, not as an expert, but as something more exciting—an adventurer in science and in the universal search for truth. For many years he was a pioneer in education. He ran a school by himself, and wrote textbooks on several subjects. As a tutor in an academy, he earned a reputation for his wide knowledge of ancient and modern languages. He became a religious leader and, as a champion of freedom in all its forms, he was involved in politics and engrossed in questions of liberty. By many he was respected, admired, and even revered; by others he was scorned, feared, hated, and reviled.

Priestley was one of those forthright characters who in their generation appear to some as enemies of society, because they are brave enough to follow the truth as they see it, wherever it may lead. The forces of law and order tend to regard such men as dangerous, for they release the forces of change. They appear even more dangerous if born into a restless age, and Priestley lived at a time when the spirit of revolution led to upheavals both in America and in Europe. In spite of all this, he is now remembered chiefly for his work in chemistry and electricity. His discoveries were of great importance, a fact that is all the more surprising when the full range of his life's work is borne in mind. Indeed, we cannot hope to understand the one without knowing something of the other.

By 1700, Yorkshire—where the story begins—was fast becoming dominated by the trades and technical arts that supported the woollen industry, then the mainstay of English commerce. The merchants and larger employers of labour were to be found mainly in the towns; but manufacturing industry was not yet divorced from farming, and many craftsmen remained in the country for miles around, retaining their hold on the land to which they turned when work for the merchants slackened. Then, as always, very many Yorkshiremen took their religion seriously. They were firmly attached to the ideals of liberty and to the new line of succession to the throne; the 'Glorious Revolution' of 1688, which, it was hoped, had put an end to gross abuses of power by the Crown, was still a vivid memory.

Priestley was descended from two typical families that looked to the Bible when searching for names to give their children. Both his grandfathers were called Joseph. The elder Joseph Priestley lived at Birstal Fieldhead, one of the white-cloth centres around Leeds, where the township merged with the open country. By trade he was a maker of cloth and a dresser, that is, he treated the woven material to give it an even texture and then singed or cut off the loose ends of fibres and finished by ironing. His house probably adjoined the workshops where he employed his tens of workmen when business was good. The family trade supplied him with the essentials of life but not many luxuries. He had been brought up a member of the Church of England, so it is said, but the family became strict Calvinist Dissenters through the influence of his wife, Sarah Healey (or Hayley), a woman of strong character. Of their eight children two sons, John and Jonas, remained at Birstal Fieldhead; and two daughters married prosperous men of Heckmondwike, about two miles to the south-west. From the point of view of obtaining orders from the merchants, the family was well situated, being roughly in the middle of a ten-mile square of which the corners were represented by Bradford, Leeds, Wakefield, and Huddersfield.

Jonas Priestley carried on the trade of dresser at the same place, but apparently on a smaller scale than his father. He married Mary, the daughter of Joseph Swift, a farmer and maltster near Shafton, some four miles beyond Wakefield. Their family increased fast, and there were already four children when Mary died in childbirth shortly after Christmas in the hard winter of 1739–40—the year of the Great Frost. Joseph, the eldest son, was born in their house on the corner of Owler Lane (Plate 1) on 13 March 1733, according to the old-style calendar (24 March new style). His brother Timothy (who became a Calvinist minister and enjoyed the patronage of Selina, Countess of Huntingdon) was born on 19 June in the following year. There was another brother, Joshua, who became a cloth-maker at Leeds. The family was completed with two sisters—Mary, who died at the age of three, and Martha, who retained a great admiration for Joseph and to whom we are indebted for many details of the family pedigree.[1]

Very little is known of Joseph's unsettled childhood apart from what he and Timothy have told. When only a few weeks old, said Timothy, Joseph was wrapped snugly in a basket and taken on horseback, with his mother, to be shown to his grandfather Swift. As a child he was much loved by all around him and mixed easily with everyone he met. Joseph remembered how his mother had taught him to be scrupulously honest —even a pin had to be returned to his Uncle John, at whose house he had picked it up when playing with his cousins, of whom there were then eight. By the time he was four his mother had taught him to repeat the catechism by heart. At about this time he was sent to stay with his grandfather at Shafton, though he was not entirely separated from his family. He did not return to live at home until after his mother's death, when he attended a neighbouring school, his brothers taking his place at Shafton for a time.

But even now he was not to know a normal family life, for his father was still a widower, and Joseph's education was anything but regular. In 1745, finding himself unable to manage his growing family single-handed, Jonas married a widow, formerly Hannah Holdsworth of Wakefield and lately house-keeper to Dr Philip Doddridge, a noted minister and tutor of an academy at Northampton. There were three daughters of the second marriage.

At the age of nine Joseph was sent to live at the Old Hall, Heckmondwike (Plate 2), the home of his father's elder sister,

---

[1] British Museum, 'Collectanea Hunteriana', Add. MS. 24607, ff. 38b, 39; also Royal Society, 'Priestley Memorial Volume'.

Sarah, who, though married for seventeen years, had no child of her own. Her husband, John Keighley, was a religious and public-spirited man of property; but his influence on the boy did not last long, for within three years he also died. Joseph remained in his aunt's sole care, and she behaved as a parent to him from that time until her death in 1764. He was sent to a number of local schools in succession, but being a natural scholar and lacking companions of his own age he soon learnt as much as the average schoolmaster could teach him. At about eleven he began to attend a free school, most probably Batley Grammar School, where Joseph Hague was usher in 1744–6. Here he made real headway with Latin and the elements of Greek.[1]

His progress was now interrupted by a serious illness, apparently tuberculosis of the lungs, and he remained 'weakly consumptive' for several years afterwards. His survival was due largely to his aunt's loving care; as Timothy said, never was a human creature more tenderly nursed. At eleven also Joseph developed a taste for trying out things, his first 'experiment' being to see how long spiders could live in bottles without change of air. There seems no reason to doubt this simple story of Timothy's, for the two boys were then meeting often and became very attached to one another.

By the age of thirteen, Joseph had read most of Bunyan's works and other religious books, as well as the familiar Latin authors, and he made a practice of writing out the sermons he heard. This habit made composition easy for him, and he learnt to write down his thoughts quickly and fluently, particularly after he had acquired shorthand. After about two years Joseph left the grammar school and began to learn Hebrew at the school of a local dissenting minister. By sixteen he had a good knowledge of the learned languages, and after that he was allowed to study on his own. He made good use of his time and formed habits of work that lasted throughout his life.

For some years his aunt had hoped that he would train for the ministry, and this explains the emphasis on languages in his education; but the state of his health now made her think

[1] The evidence is discussed by D. N. R. Lester, *The History of Batley Grammar School*, Batley, 1962, 48–50.

BIRTH PLACE OF DR PRIESTLEY.

(from a Photograph in possession of the Rev. Edmund Kell.)

Plate 1 The house at Birstal Fieldhead, near Leeds, where Joseph Priestley was born. This lithograph was made from an early photograph taken shortly before the building was demolished. (*Dr Williams's Library*)

Plate 2 The Old Hall, Heckmondwike, near Birstal, where Priestley spent his boyhood with his aunt, Sarah Keighley. For part of this time he attended the Grammar School at nearby Batley. (*Courtesy The Headmaster, Batley Grammar School*)

that a commercial career might be more suitable. Game as ever, and always intent on learning something new, he began to prepare himself by studying French, German, and Italian. He did not have long for this, and he was soon sent to the home of an uncle, a merchant, for whom he acted as translator and wrote letters in French and German. It was intended that he should go to a counting-house in Lisbon for further experience, but when everything was ready he suddenly decided that his health was now good enough for him to think again of the ministry, or possibly medicine, as a career. This meant attending the full course at one of the dissenting academies.

Accordingly, in 1752 he went as the first student to be enrolled at the new academy at Daventry directed by Dr Caleb Ashworth, the academy at Northampton having ceased when Doddridge died in the previous October. The alternative to Daventry—an academy run by Zephaniah Marryat at Plasterers' Hall, London, and, after 1754, by Dr John Conder at Mile End—did not please him, for he had already developed strongly independent religious views and would have nothing more to do with the strict and somewhat sombre Calvinism of Timothy, the rest of the family, and the Mile End Academy, as it was later called.

While waiting to enter Daventry he spent two days in the week with a dissenting minister named Haggerston(e), who lived some four miles away. Haggerston had been educated under the mathematician Colin Maclaurin, professor in the University of Edinburgh, a friend and protégé of Isaac Newton and one of the foremost exponents and developers of his mathematical ideas. Joseph was introduced by Haggerston to the various branches of mathematics, and then began to read books on physics, logic, and philosophy. Timothy said that he derived much pleasure from experimenting with levers: 'he soon told me how many men he could lift from the ground'. The latter part of each week he spent teaching Hebrew to a Baptist minister at Gildersome, near Leeds. By this means he greatly increased his own knowledge, for his mental appetite was insatiable, and he found time also to study Chaldee and Syriac, and began to learn Arabic.

So by the time Daventry Academy was ready, Joseph was

older and much better equipped than the majority of students, many of whom left by the time they reached his age. He was thus excused the first year's work and much of the second. Since he was a keen scholar, advanced in knowledge and with no falsely humble estimate of his own abilities, it is not surprising that the few comments to come down from his fellow-students are not especially flattering. He seems to have been more serious than the average and somewhat aloof from the younger students, who must have seemed very immature to him.

The dissenting academies occupied an important place in eighteenth-century education, for the old universities of England did not freely admit any but members of the Anglican Church until 1872. Dissenters, it should be remembered, included not only nonconformist Protestants who could not conscientiously subscribe to the articles of the Anglican Church, but also Catholics, Jews, and Quakers, whose sons were normally debarred from preparing for the ministry or the professions in the universities. Many of them, therefore, attended the academies, and several of those who could afford it completed their education in Scotland, for example in medicine or law at Edinburgh, or on the Continent. Both Anglicans and Dissenters had their strict adherents and their broad-minded latitudinarians; the dissenting academies reflected these differences, some imposing what amounted to religious tests of their own, whereas others were 'free', accepting Anglicans and others without discrimination. Some of the latter enjoyed an atmosphere of intellectual freedom unknown among the orthodox of all denominations.

In this movement towards greater freedom Dr Isaac Watts, the hymn-writer, exerted a notable influence. Watts was the author of a catechism widely used among Dissenters, and he wrote textbooks that had a considerable vogue; but he was chiefly admired for his devotion to civil and religious liberty. His philosophy of education and his belief in the value of free thought and discussion on all subjects, including religion, greatly influenced Doddridge, at whose academy all sides of controversial questions were openly examined. These somewhat novel tendencies were carried over to Daventry under Caleb Ashworth, and it was this true freedom to study, think, and discuss that attracted Priestley, for he had already developed an intense distaste for dogma, from whatever source it came. This attitude seems to date from the time when he was refused admission to membership of the chapel attended by his aunt because he was unable to show due repentance for the sin of Adam and to give a sufficiently 'spiritual' account of his religious experiences.

The drabness and restricted facilities of Daventry, in comparison with Oxford and Cambridge, meant little to those who in any event were excluded from the universities, whereas to men of Priestley's stamp three years of uninterrupted study, with no subject of inquiry frowned upon, were delightful in the extreme. Here he became convinced that the life of a Christian minister was the noblest of all professions, and he set out to prepare himself to the utmost of his ability. The normal work of the classes was not enough for him. Every day he conquered a minimum of ten folio pages of Greek, in company with his fellow-student Alexander of Birmingham, who was later a noted Greek scholar and Bible critic. In addition he read widely and methodically, planning in advance the work to be done. Though Daventry had no special facilities for science, Priestley was always interested in mathematical and 'philosophical' pursuits and continued his earlier studies in these fields, not forgetting subjects of importance to medicine, which was ever a strong interest, though nothing more. Thus he began to read Boerhaave's classic treatise on chemistry, the *Elementa Chemiae*, of which the last English edition was printed in 1753.

While at Daventry he also began to write various manuscripts that were eventually published as books. The most important was his *Institutes of Natural and Revealed Religion*, drafted in 1755 but not printed until seventeen years later. All of it, he tells us, was thoroughly discussed with Samuel Clark, the sub-tutor. It was this methodical way of working and the continual accumulation of materials that afterwards made it possible for him to work on several books on different subjects at once, so that it was misleadingly said that he could write books faster than other people could read them. Often the manuscripts had been lying by him for many years. He also knew the advantages of composing in shorthand, for he was thus able to develop a natural style of writing which, though sometimes lacking in polish, was easy to follow and carried the reader forward with speed.

By far the most formative book that came his way at Daventry was David Hartley's *Observations on Man*, which had appeared in 1749. Here, in the first few pages, he was introduced to a new world of philosophical ideas and to the great thinkers and systematic writers on science and medicine of the previous generation, particularly Locke (1632–1704), Newton (1643–1727), Stahl (1660–1734), and Boerhaave (1668–1738). Hartley's theory of man and human nature was based primarily on ideas he found in Newton and Locke. At the end of his *Opticks*, Newton had listed a number of 'Queries', among which he suggested that light falling upon the retina in the eye set up vibrations that were carried to the brain along the optic nerve. Hartley extended this idea to explain all the senses. From Locke he took the view that mental activity proceeds by means of association. Assuming Newton's vibrations and Locke's association of ideas, Hartley was able to give a comprehensive account of man's nature that was widely accepted and admired in the second half of the eighteenth century. For example the names David Hartley were given by Coleridge to one of his sons.

Gradually Priestley became imbued with the thoughts of Hartley, Newton, and Locke, and they pervaded his outlook to the end of his days. If we are to understand him, we must have some idea of what they stood for. Hartley, though a great Christian philosopher, did not think of man as a trinity of body, mind, and soul. His first sentence made the bald statement that 'Man consists of Two Parts, Body and Mind'. Insensibly Priestley also began to think that way, eventually believing that the soul had no existence apart from the body. In his view the mind and soul were one, and the mind did not exist when the brain ceased to function. Today it is difficult to understand the upheaval that such ideas were to bring about, though many still regard them as heretical.

John Locke's works, particularly his *Essay concerning Human Understanding* and *The Reasonableness of Christianity*, taught ideas that leaned towards Unitarianism ('Onegoddism', as Coleridge called it); they were widely read by Dissenters throughout the eighteenth century. Religion, Locke maintained, must be tested by reason; if it contradicted any self-evident truth it must be regarded as false. To many in his day it seemed dangerous to claim that reason rather than authority should form the basis of religion, or that to disregard the conclusions of reason was the height of impiety. It may have been dangerous from the point of view of the State and the established Church; but it was a manly and progressive outlook; Priestley absorbed it and acted upon it with more honesty and openness than any other man of his generation, even though it led to persecution and eventually to voluntary exile.

From the works of Newton, a friend of Locke, Priestley learnt not only the rules and principles of natural philosophy but also religious views that could not have come from a Trinitarian. Newton, who was regarded as an authority on early Christian history, was antagonistic to the concept of the Trinity as taught by Athanasius. Indeed Newton's most important work in theology was a piece of textual criticism entitled *An Historical Account of Two Notable Corruptions of the Scriptures*, a study that was known to Locke and was intended for publication anonymously. But Newton decided to suppress it, and it was not printed until 1754, and then only from a copy that had been preserved in Holland. The passages that Newton considered to be later additions were the so-called 'proof-texts' of the Trinity, and his arguments helped to strengthen the hands of the Unitarians, or Socinians, as they were then generally called.

By the time Priestley left Daventry he was an accomplished scholar and had shown plenty of ability for independent work. In addition to his theological studies he was well versed in philosophy, had read fairly widely in history, mathematics, and science, and had acquired a working knowledge of six ancient and three modern languages. He had already broken away for ever from the mental shackles of orthodox Calvinism, and each book that gave him a new and wider horizon left an indelible imprint on his mind. The mental associations that were to determine his future thought were already formed, though he still had far to go before reaching the outlook in which he finally rested, if rested is a word that can be used for a man whose thirst for new knowledge was never quenched.

Having completed his course he eagerly awaited a call, not then caring in the least where it might lead him. He gladly answered it when it came, and he left Daventry in 1755 to be an assistant minister to a congregation at Needham Market, Suffolk. Here he learnt painfully the effect of a 'low despised situation' on a man of character and ambition, though his youth and good spirits enabled him to put up with it. It was not to be expected that an intense young man full of learning could make much headway in a simple country community; the contrast between them was too great. He also made a number of unprofitable moves. By refusing help from bodies whose opinions he could not countenance, he reduced his guaranteed salary to thirty pounds a year, and even this his congregation found itself scarcely able to pay. Indeed, had it not been for George Benson (an uncle of his fellow-student Alexander) and his friend Andrew Kippis, who had funds at their disposal to help indigent ministers in their first few years, he might well have suffered greatly from sheer lack of food, for he was still enough of a student to pay as much as three guineas for a book that he wanted.

Another setback occurred when, in his desire to serve his congregation, he gave a course of lectures to them on the 'Institutes', or theory of religion, based on what he had written at Daventry. When he came to speak of the unity of God they listened only to see if his views on the Trinity were 'sound'. At that time, as he afterwards admitted, he was a 'furious freethinker', and this was soon discovered. As a result, his congregation fell away, and with their going his salary dwindled too. Though he had not the slightest desire to teach, necessity drove him to announce his intention to run a school, but not a single pupil came to him. In addition to this, his aunt's allowances ceased because of stories about him that had reached her through his 'orthodox relations', Timothy by his own account being at least in part responsible for this.

To cap it all, he was greatly distressed by a hereditary impediment in his speech, which, not surprisingly, had very much worsened during his stay at Needham. He found it almost impossible to preach, and this seemed to be taking away from him any opportunity there might be of finding a more congenial situation. Through the generosity of his aunt, who responded to a special appeal, he was able to go to London for a course of treatment offered by Mr Angier for a fee of twenty guineas; this consisted of breathing exercises and of practising to read slowly and distinctly. By this means he largely checked the stammer, and afterwards was careful to avoid being seriously hampered by it. On this visit he obtained introductions to his benefactors, Kippis and Benson.

On the credit side, Priestley had ample time at Needham for further study and was invited by a Quaker to use his library whenever he wished. He also made occasional visits to Cambridge. He found time to look more closely at the basis of his own theological beliefs; this involved him in detailed Biblical analysis and textual criticism, and led to several new manuscripts, some of which were published in later years. As a result he moved still further along the path of independent thought, and slowly extended the circle of his intellectual acquaintance. He corresponded with David Hartley about the application of his philosophical ideas to education, and Hartley promised to help him if he decided to publish anything on the matter. But in 1757 Hartley died.

Hope of a change of occupation came with the news that a new academy, on a quite different plan from any that had preceded it, was being opened at Warrington in Lancashire, with well-known people as subscribers and trustees—men like Dr John Roebuck and James Percival, then of Manchester, and Thomas Bentley of Liverpool. Roebuck is now remembered chiefly for his development of basic industries, such as the manufacture of iron and sulphuric acid, the Percivals for their connection with literary and scientific developments, and Bentley as the art connoisseur and, later, the business partner of Josiah Wedgwood the potter. In 1757 the trustees were considering the appointment of tutors, and Priestley was among those nominated by the subscribers for the post of tutor in languages. His name had been put forward by Benson, with the support of Kippis, Clark, and others, who described him as a young gentleman of unexceptionable character, devoted to the principles of civil and religious liberty, and remarkable for the extent of his critical and classical learning, uncommon in one of his age. On this occasion the election went against him, as he lacked teaching experience and was known to have an impediment in his speech. Nevertheless his name had been brought to the notice of the trustees, and this helped him in the long run. Warrington, indeed, was destined to play a most important role in his career.

Most of his studies at Needham had been classical, mathematical, and theological; he had kept up his reading in experimental science, but was handicapped by having no money for apparatus. The failure of his attempt to start a school was most discouraging, but he had more success after he had obtained some globes and arranged a course of twelve lectures on their use, the fee being half a guinea for each person. This more than paid for the globes, and he next decided to give other courses on various branches of science, so as to build up a good set of instruments and apparatus.

In the event, this was not necessary. Knowing of his unpleasant existence in Suffolk, his friends elsewhere had not been idle. An opportunity to move came through a distant relative of his mother's who secured for him an invitation to preach a trial sermon at Sheffield. He did not prove acceptable, however, and this would surely have dampened his enthusiasm for the ministry had not a minister there, the Rev. Thomas Haynes, offered to recommend him to his former congregation at Nantwich in Cheshire, on the other side of the country from Needham, where he could rely on staying for at least a year. And so in 1758 he left Needham, going by sea to London, as this was the cheapest way, and then travelling overland. He was now twenty-five, and this escape was a great turning-point in his career. He travelled light for, apart from the manuscripts of his own composition, his globes, and the books he had preferred to food, he had no possessions.

Chapter 2

Teacher and Tutor

NANTWICH was more akin to Birstal than to Needham, for it
was a centre of the local manufacture—Cheshire salt. At the
Wiches (Nantwich, Northwich, and Middlewich) 'white' salt
was made from rock-salt and brine, and from the Nantwich
area rock-salt was sent down the river Weaver to the Mersey
and converted to 'common' salt on the Dungeon coast and at
Liverpool. Here, at the flow of the tide, sea-water was passed
into lead cisterns and crushed rock-salt dissolved in it. After
settling, the strong brine was run off into pans holding up to
800 gallons apiece and slowly evaporated with the aid of a fire.
The refined salts were shipped from Liverpool in large quantities to various parts of Great Britain and Ireland and to the
American colonies.[1]

Probably it was at Nantwich that Priestley first became
familiar with the name of William Brownrigg, a physician at
Whitehaven whose book, *The Art of Making Common Salt*, had
been published in 1748. Brownrigg, in an interesting preface,
reminded his readers that Bacon had taught how necessary was
a knowledge of the 'mechanic arts' to the creation of a true
science of nature—'which is not taken up in vain and fruitless
speculations, but effectually labours to relieve the necessities of
human life'. Whether or not this book had a direct influence
on Priestley, his interest in science grew while he was at
Nantwich, and Bacon's view of the purpose of science became
the yardstick by which he gauged the importance of much of
his later work.

A few miles to the east of Nantwich ran the road from the
Potteries to the bridge over the Mersey at Warrington and

[1] For an early description see W. Jackson, 'Some Inquiries concerning the
Salt-springs and the way of salt-making at Nantwich in Cheshire', *Phil. Trans.*,
1669, *4*, 1060.

thence to Liverpool. Throughout the summer it was busy with wagons carrying salt from Cheshire to the Midlands and various manufactured goods to towns in Lancashire. The winter was relatively quiet, for the roads were frequently unsuitable for heavy wheeled traffic and as yet there was no adequate system of canals. Then the wagoners turned to other pursuits. For example, William Bass, one of Wedgwood's drivers and more enterprising than most, spent the winter producing home-made beer at his house in Burton-on-Trent. In time this became so well known that he gave up his wagon and developed the business still associated with his name.

In Nantwich Priestley found a happier atmosphere and little bickering about points of religion. Many of his hearers were travelling packmen, especially Scots, and so he continually met new faces. On the other hand, there were few people with whom he could make lasting friendships, and he therefore decided to devote his time to work and especially to remedying his lack of teaching experience. Now success attended everything he did. His hearers took kindly enough to his preaching, and when he announced his intention to open a school there was a gratifying response, for education of the kind he proposed to give was not easily found in that area. Soon he had about thirty boys and six girls, the latter being taught in a separate room. Somewhat to his surprise, he found great satisfaction in the work and discovered that a deep-seated desire to share knowledge with others lay at the root of his success. Both master and pupils worked hard. Lessons began at seven in the morning and went on to four in the afternoon, with an hour's break for dinner, except for 'red-letter' days, which were allowed as holidays.

Priestley's income was now enough to cover the cost, not only of the books he needed, but also of certain scientific instruments—an air-pump, an electrical machine, a selection of microscopes, and so on—and he taught the top class how to use and look after them. When parents and friends visited the school they had the novel experience of being entertained with experiments and short lectures given by the pupils themselves. Priestley quickly saw the value of such training and found that it added greatly to the school's reputation.

In this part of his work he was helped by his friendship with the Rev. Joseph Brereton, the diminutive Vicar of nearby Acton. A Suffolk man, he was educated at Cambridge where he was known as 'the Little Man of Queen's'. Brereton, it was said, was a man of strong passions and great talents, and he had made a deep study of every branch of useful science. He had a room set apart for Priestley, and here the latter spent many an evening, often staying for the night. Priestley remembered him with affection, and more than thirty years later he wrote: 'a common love of science brought us acquainted, and I have . . . a telescope, made with his own hands, which he gave me as a token of his friendship'.

Priestley had little leisure for scientific work, for after school hours he was private tutor to the family of a wealthy attorney. Yet he did learn to relax a little and, at the suggestion of John Eddowes, with whom he boarded, he began to play the flute, from which he derived much pleasure and amusement at odd moments for many years to come.[1]

Apart from science, Priestley gave special attention to English, mathematics, and history, for reasons that require explaining. In the grammar schools much emphasis was placed on Latin and Greek, as without them it was impossible to prepare for the English universities and thus for Church and State appointments. For the generality of Dissenters, on the other hand, a career in industry or commerce was far more likely, and so mathematics and English, taught mainly in the commercial schools, were at least of equal importance to the classical languages. There was a tendency for these subjects to be neglected in the grammar schools, scholars sometimes being better able to write in Latin than in their mother tongue. What Priestley's pupils needed was the ability to write plain English correctly and fluently. Thus he was interested not so much in the finer points of grammar, nor in the polished style being cultivated by writers such as Samuel Johnson, but in what today would be called 'use of English'. Priestley's course, with the title *Rudiments of English Grammar*, was printed for his pupils in 1761. After-

[1] J. Hall, *A History of the Town and Parish of Nantwich, or Wich-Malbank*, Nantwich, 1883, *passim*.

wards the book was enlarged, and it remained in print for half a century.

At this time also he began to think about teaching the young something of the history of mankind and particularly of their own country. In this field little had been done apart from the history of Greece and Rome, studied in connection with the classical languages. Nor were there many aids for pupils in the form of charts or books. First he began to prepare a comprehensive wall-chart showing the life-spans of men distinguished in various fields. But before he had completed this, he was approached by the rector of the Warrington Academy and one of the trustees and invited to become a tutor there in the languages and belles lettres. This was an opportunity he could scarcely refuse, though he would have preferred to teach mathematics and science, which by now interested him more than any other subjects. A formal letter was sent to him on 25 June 1761 and he accepted, despite the fact that his income, for a time at least, would be reduced.

There is no doubt that his success as a teacher was the means whereby he had come before the public eye, for the trustees' report for that year mentioned specially that the new tutor had 'attended to the duties of a private school with indefatigable labour' and had 'discovered a singular genius for the management of youth'. They said he was an amiable person of an open and benevolent disposition, and a man of great accomplishments, real piety, and outstanding industry; he was an able master of the learned languages and had considerable proficiency in many of the modern ones as well.

When his successor at Nantwich had taken over the school and some of its equipment, such as his globes, Priestley left for Warrington. In due course a few of his older pupils followed him there; they included William, son of Isaac Wilkinson the ironmaster, owner of the forge at Bersham near Wrexham.[1] Priestley was well known to the family, which then lived at Plâs Grono (formerly the home of Elihu Yale, founder of Yale University), and William's sister Mary, a girl of about seventeen, had succeeded in winning the admiration

---

[1] A. N. Palmer, *A History of the Town and Parish of Wrexham*, Wrexham, Pt. III, 1888, 135; Pt. V, 1903, 256.

and affection of the young minister and schoolmaster (*see* Plate 3).

At Warrington the Academy was housed in a rather austere building on the south bank of the Mersey, then an unpolluted stream that offered good sport, including salmon, to the enthusiastic angler. A progressive atmosphere pervaded the place; a new building was being erected to provide more suitable amenities for work of university standard, and this, together with houses for the tutors, with whom most of the students were to be lodged, was to form an academic precinct separate from the town (Plate 4). Warrington was already bustling, its growth having resulted largely from its manufacture of coarse linens and checks. In recent years several manufacturers had changed over from linen to sail-cloth, and the town later provided about half of the heavy-grade material required by the navy. The hemp and flax used were brought by boat from Liverpool, where it was imported from Russia. Other regular trades included the making of pins, locks, and hinges, and at times copper-smelting, sugar-refining, glass-making, and foundry work were carried on in the vicinity. As all travellers to Liverpool and the north by road had to pass through Warrington, the town had a considerable number of inns. Thus malting and brewing were also of importance in that area. These various activities, while making it desirable to separate the Academy from the town as much as possible, served as a reminder that the chief purpose of education there was 'preparation for civil and active life'.

Priestley lost no time in putting his educational views into practice and in devising courses of study appropriate to the Academy's avowed aims. His industry was phenomenal. He already had pretty clear ideas as to what was demanded in English, and this now had to be extended to include oratory and criticism. He was experienced in teaching languages and had various ideas about the introduction of history and geography. The object of the science teaching there had already been made clear in the trustees' report for the previous year.

The Improvement of Natural Knowledge upon the Foundation of Experiment seems to be an Object which engages the Notice of the learned in all Parts of the World; and if to the common Experiments in Philosophy [physics], could be added some of the more important Processes in Chemistry, especially that Part of it which has a Connection with our Manufactures and Commerce, it would probably have the best Effect.

In the report for 1762 the widened scope of the Academy's activities was outlined. It shows that Priestley's own account of his work there was a modest one, and that in no point did he exaggerate the importance of his contributions to its success.

In the Latin Class the Classics are read; Latin Compositions made; and a course of Roman Antiquities, and Mythology gone through.

In the Greek Class are read the Greek authors, and a Course of Greek Antiquities.

Those young Gentlemen who learn French are taught to read and write that Language; and go through a Course of Exercises calculated to prepare them to converse in it.

The English Grammar is taught to the younger Students, and they are trained up in a regular Course of English Compositions.

By the Tutor in this Department are read Lectures on Logick; the Theory of Language, and Universal Grammar; Oratory and Criticism; the Study of History; and Anatomy.

He also directs the public Academical Exercises, consisting of Translations from Greek, Latin, and French Authors; and Orations, or Dissertations, which are delivered alternately in English, and Latin or French; wherein a particular Attention is paid to the Manner of Reading and Speaking.

It would be difficult to find a broader interpretation of 'languages and belles lettres' than this. Some of the work was new in conception and was certainly not a repetition of the curriculum to be found in any other centre of learning. Part of his aim was to bring in a great variety of miscellaneous information of use to a man going out into the world. Several of the courses were published—at least in outline—in later years, though he was modest enough to wait for a demand to show itself before going into print, and then only if the course contained material of sufficient originality. Thus the first of these books was printed in 1762 and the last in 1788. In his *Rudiments of English Grammar* he had found it necessary even to justify setting English compositions for students, as it was commonly objected that for the young this was like trying to make bricks without straw. He insisted that all schools—grammar schools particularly — must introduce English grammar, English composition, and frequent English translations from other languages. He added his praise of Samuel Johnson's recent and justly famed English dictionary which, he said, had been of the greatest use to him, and hoped that Johnson would go on to do as much for the grammar of the language as he had in giving precision to its tools. But Johnson never responded to this invitation.

In 1762 Priestley's new course on the *Theory of Language, and Universal Grammar* was published at Warrington in a form suitable for class use. It was an outline only, to be filled in by the tutor. He did not get far without mentioning his two favourite authors—Newton and Hartley. He often pointed out that the English language had only been 'fixed' within living memory—during the reign of Queen Anne—and that its very simplicity gave it a good chance of being preserved unchanged 'to the latest ages'. Again he praised Johnson for his work.

The trustees of the Academy thought it would be a good thing to have Priestley's lectures on oratory and criticism published at their expense, the proceeds from the sale of the work being received by them to offset the cost. We may well imagine this did not please Priestley, who was jealous of his compositions, even in manuscript. No more courses, indeed, were released while he remained a tutor at Warrington. These particular lectures were eventually printed in 1777 and revealed a degree of sensitivity and perception that surprised his critics. The course was more comprehensive than anything that had previously been done, the arrangement of the material was new and the theory original in many respects. He thought the subject admirably illustrated Hartley's notions on the association of ideas.

Once again he kept the reader alert with illustrations drawn from various fields. In his *Grammar* he had introduced thoughts about science, and here he found occasion to give opinions about history. 'Unless history be read either with a view to gain a knowledge of mankind, in order to form our own conduct; or with some scientific view, in order to determine some important subject of rational inquiry, it is nothing better than reading

romance.' But he did not lack humour—in fact he was one of
the few authors to write constructively about it. As an example
of double contrast, he suddenly presented the following couplet:

> Beneath this stone my wife doth lie:
> She's now at rest, and so am I.

Priestley's most original work in the educational field was the
introduction of various aspects of history—political, economic,
social, and the like—as a means of forming good citizens.
'With this view,' he wrote, 'I planned and composed three
courses, one on *history in general,* another on *the history of England,*
and a third on *the laws and constitution of England.*' Though a
synopsis of the courses was published in 1765, the outline text
appeared only in 1788, with the title *Lectures on History, and
General Policy.* By general policy he meant everything that
contributed to make 'the great societies of mankind happy,
numerous, and secure, with which young men of fortune cannot
be too well acquainted'. It dealt with such matters as laws,
government, industry, commerce, and armed forces, and was
intended to provide a background of value to a future statesman, military commander, lawyer, merchant, or accomplished country gentleman. This, he had to point out to the
critics, was not the same thing as 'teaching politics to low
mechanics and manufacturers'. In these lectures there were
references to the interplay between the arts and sciences. The
sciences at that time were leading to numerous improvements
in the useful arts, and the arts in turn were promoting 'society
and humanity', which again favoured the progress of science in
all its branches.

Another lecture showed how the dates of early historical
events could be computed from eclipses. This had only a short
introduction, as he used to carry out calculations based on
several past eclipses to show how the method was used.
Chronological charts were produced as aids to memory, and
sometimes models were brought along to help the students to
visualize their history. Thus the lecture on fortifications was
centred around a wooden model. There were also hints of
possible reforms; for example, he suggested that the best way of

Plate 3 Plâs Grono, near Wrexham, the home of Isaac Wilkinson, ironmaster, where Priestley met his future wife, Mary. It was formerly the home of Elihu Yale, founder of Yale College (now Yale University). The house was demolished shortly after this sketch was made in 1876.

Plate 4 Warrington Academy in 1762. (*Courtesy The Chief Librarian, County Borough of Warrington*)

dealing with the problem of the poor might be to make them provide for themselves by withholding a proportion of their wages and putting it aside for their use in old age. These courses were full of lively thought, and were afterwards used not only in other dissenting institutions, but also in some American colleges; they were even recommended later by the professor of history at Cambridge.

Priestley lived on terms of great friendship with the rector, John Seddon, the theological tutor, John Aikin, and the tutor in mathematics and natural philosophy, John Holt. He also made lifelong friendships with several of the students and other young people, particularly Thomas Percival, who had already completed his studies there, and Aikin's two gifted children— John, the well-known physician and writer, and Anna Laetitia, afterwards the poetess Mrs Barbauld. The younger set radiated gaiety; soon Priestley was taking a hand in arranging plays, and other social activities followed. In later life Mrs Barbauld recalled that there had been no narrowness at Warrington. 'Dancing, cards, the theatres, were all held lawful in moderation.' The orthodox Calvinists were shocked.

By the spring of 1762, when the completion of its new building was within sight, the Academy found itself in difficulties owing to religious differences among the subscribers. In April, Seddon was in London seeking assistance from influential people, and during his absence Priestley took over his duties as minister at Warrington.[1] He was also concerned with trying to arrange for students to attend a public chemistry lecture, and with obtaining some lenses for Brereton through Seddon's acquaintance, John Canton, F.R.S., a physicist and schoolmaster in London, and a former friend of Doddridge. This first attempt to introduce chemistry seems to have been unsuccessful, for not even the name of the lecturer was recorded.

In May, Priestley told Seddon that he was seriously preparing for ordination, in view of his impending marriage and the unsettled state of the Academy's affairs.

I can sincerely say, I never knew what it was to be anxious on my own account; but I cannot help confessing I begin to feel a good

---

[1] Letters written during this period were printed in the *Christian Reformer*, 1854, *10* (N.S.), 625 ff.

deal on the account of another person. The hazard of bringing a person into difficulties which she cannot probably have any idea or prospect of, affects me at times very sensibly.

But Seddon's mission was at least partially successful, and Warrington students were now to be eligible for exhibitions from the Presbyterian Fund. Priestley also suggested that Seddon should enlist the help of Samuel Chandler, F.R.S., one of the most influential dissenting divines, and obtain from him a written statement to the effect that he approved the Academy's work.

With the completion of the new building, a house became available to Priestley as one of the tutors, and he decided to set up a home, although this would mean providing accommodation for some of the students. On 23 June 1762, at Wrexham parish church, he married the young Mary Wilkinson, a well-read girl of strong character who proved an admirable wife for him in all respects. The house was not entirely to her liking, however, for it was necessary to provide even locks and grates, and to paper all the walls.

Priestley was now able to make frequent visits to Liverpool, where he went as the guest of Thomas Bentley who lived in the then fashionable Paradise Street, a quarter that did not suffer from the great fire that ravaged the town in 1762. Bentley was a man of substance and held a standing brief to represent the Corporation in all important business in London and before Parliament. He abhorred the slave trade, for which Liverpool was then notorious; had been a founder of a public library there in 1758; and, with his surgeon friend Matthew Turner, had helped to found the Liverpool Academy of Art. He numbered various artists and portrait painters among his acquaintance.[1]

In the same year Josiah Wedgwood, travelling from Burslem to Liverpool on horseback, suffered a fall near the bridge at Warrington, but insisted on finishing his journey and then called for Turner to treat his damaged leg. For Wedgwood the accident meant several weeks of enforced rest, and Turner, finding him a most interesting character, introduced Bentley to

[1] R.B. [Richard Bentley], *Thomas Bentley 1730–1780 of Liverpool, Etruria, and London*, Guildford, 1927, *passim*.

him. As a result of this, Wedgwood became a visitor to Paradise Street, and Priestley became well known to them all. Arising from these contacts, Turner was introduced by Priestley to Warrington as one who could meet their needs as a lecturer in chemistry and anatomy, and he gave courses at the Academy in 1763-5. His chemistry course was something after Priestley's own heart, though it was his first introduction to the practical side of the subject. He attended the lectures and helped with the practical demonstrations, afterwards calling on Turner for further tuition. The trustees' report for 1763 said:

> This last spring Mr. Turner of Liverpool, a gentleman deservedly esteemed for his abilities as a Chemist, went through a full course of practical and commercial Chemistry in the Academy, very much to the satisfaction of all who attended him. A room is properly fitted up, and an useful apparatus provided for the cultivation of this most valuable branch of natural knowledge: and Mr. Turner will continue to favour the Academy with his assistance in this way, as often as shall be thought convenient.

With all his courses to attend to, and lecturing as he was for nearly the whole day, Priestley was not yet able to find time for practical science on his own account. He considered that his proposed biographical chart, begun at Nantwich, and his other educational schemes were of more immediate consequence. The Academy's President, Lord Willoughby of Parham, showed an interest in the chart and suggested that if Priestley ran into any difficulties he should write to Thomas Birch, a Secretary of the Royal Society, for assistance. This he did when, at last, in July 1764, the chart was being engraved for publication, and two sets of dates were still lacking—for a Tartar prince and an Arabian poet.[1] He asked Birch to examine the chart, which the engraver would show to him, and to ask Lord Willoughby's permission to dedicate it to him:

> I feel I cannot ask him myself; none of my friends will have any opportunity of doing it in time, and you will soon see him in his way through London.

The *Chart of Biography* met with immediate success; it went through many editions, and was still in print in the 1820s.

[1] British Museum, Sloane MS. 4317, f. 42.

His friends at Warrington and elsewhere, recognizing the value of his work for education, tried to secure for him an honorary degree. A recommendation was drawn up and signed by Lord Willoughby and Samuel Chandler, and sent to the University of Edinburgh.[1] Thomas Percival, then studying medicine at Edinburgh, took up the case with the Principal, who was readily convinced of the justice of making such a mark of distinction.[2] The University records show that the degree of Doctor of Laws was conferred upon the Rev. Joseph Priestley, 'Teacher of Languages and Belles Lettres in the Academy of Warrington', on 4 December 1764. This recognition was to prove the spur for even greater efforts.

While he was engaged on the chart, Priestley was also working on an *Essay on a course of liberal education for civil and active life*, which was intended to justify the kind of courses that had been introduced at Warrington. In his hands the three main influences in education—the religious, intellectual, and utilitarian—were combined to give what became the basic type of grammar school education over a long period. The subjects he included as essential were Latin (as being of more direct use than Greek), English, French, and Mathematics, together with physics (natural philosophy) and chemistry. To the arts subjects he added history, and to the sciences, geography.

Had Priestley, with his broad philosophical approach, done no more than this, it would have ensured him a place in the annals of education. But it has all been largely forgotten, or at least overshadowed, by the scientific career on which he was shortly to embark. In all his books and lecture courses there had been references to science, but hitherto, apart from his contact with Turner, his chief interest had been electricity. Now he began to look at this subject in a new light—as an educationist and historian.

In the history of human affairs, he said, vices and miseries were 'the most glaring and striking objects'; divine providence ever bringing good out of evil was the other side of the picture. Some preferred natural history—the contemplation of uniformity and variety, as he termed it—but this also tended to

---

[1] Bodleian MS. Eng. Misc. c. 132, f. 1.
[2] T. Percival, *Works*, London, 1807, i, p. xl.

become tedious. The history of science, on the other hand, enjoyed the advantages of both while being relieved of their less pleasing aspects. It showed the powers of Nature being discovered and directed by human skill; and conspicuous through it all was real progress and improvement. He concluded that a history of experimental philosophy was one of the great needs of the time. It would be an immense undertaking —more than one man ought to attempt; but if he made a start with electricity, others might do the same for other subjects. It would be an unusual historical task, for the subject itself was scarcely half a century old and many of the chief discoverers were still alive. It was the kind of task that most historians shun.

With such thoughts in mind, Priestley asked Seddon to write him a letter of introduction to John Canton who had done original work in electricity and, as a Fellow of the Royal Society, enjoyed a wide acquaintance in the world of science and could arrange the other introductions Priestley would need. Armed with the letter, dated 18 December 1765, Priestley took the coach for London, thrilled with the prospect of meeting active men of science. He did not as yet expect to make contributions of his own to this work, but he did hope that his book would be of use to scientists and instructive to students of natural philosophy.

Chapter 3

Adventurer in Natural Philosophy

On arrival in London, Priestley lost no time in seeking out Canton, who invited him to spend Christmas as his guest. Seddon had described Priestley as a sensible man with a considerable share of learning and a taste for natural philosophy, and Canton soon introduced him to various scientific friends who in course of time became intimates of Priestley's also. They included Benjamin Franklin, then in England as the agent of the government of Pennsylvania; Richard Price, a mathematician and pioneer of insurance; and Dr Watson, an active 'electrician'. In their company he probably had his first taste of London's social life, for they were the central figures of a club, composed mainly of physicians, dissenting clergy, and masters of academies, which met at St Paul's Coffee-house in St Paul's Churchyard. This was near the home of the bookseller, Johnson, who became Priestley's publisher. Another of Priestley's ambitions was realized on 9 January 1766, when Price took him as his guest to a meeting of the Royal Society. No wonder that after his return to Warrington, Priestley told Canton that his memory of the visit seemed like a pleasing dream. 'I frequently enjoy it once again in recollection, and ardently wish for a repetition of it.'

Franklin had a high reputation in electrical science. His main experimental work was done in the years 1747–55 and published by the Royal Society, of which he became a Fellow in 1756. Apart from his invention of the lightning conductor for the protection of buildings, he had carried out much work on the charging of Leyden jars and on atmospheric electricity in general.

William Watson had been active during the same period. In 1747 he aroused the public interest by passing an electric discharge through the Thames near Westminster Bridge. He also found that Leyden jars were much more effective for storing electric charge if coated with metal foil both inside and out. About 1750 Watson noticed the luminous effect when electricity was discharged through a long glass tube from which the air had been pumped out, an observation that led eventually to the discovery of cathode rays and X-rays. Watson's discoveries were important and various, and were repeated by Franklin and others in America.

Priestley's introduction to Price and to two of the most successful exponents of practical electricity provided him with just those intimate contacts that he needed for the success of his plan. He mentioned the proposed history to Franklin and received every encouragement—far beyond what he had expected—for he took back with him to Warrington many suggestions for further experiments that needed to be carried out, together with hints that led him to repeat much of the earlier work. As a result, his descriptions were often vivid and showed a complete mastery of the techniques involved. A separate room at Warrington was already equipped for experiments, and he attacked his self-imposed task with an enthusiasm that impressed even those who were familiar with his frequent bursts of energy. 'Human happiness,' he wrote, 'depends chiefly upon having some object to pursue, and upon the vigour with which our faculties are exerted in the pursuit.' For hours each day for some months he turned the handle of his electrical machine to charge his batteries of Leyden jars, which, after each discharge, had to be charged again. If his definition of happiness was correct, he must have been happy indeed. But at last he became 'fatigued with the incessant charging of the electrical battery, and stunned with the frequent report of its explosion'.

Already in the early days of 1766 he was furiously at work, possibly even before he left London, and on 14 February he was able to give Canton an account of his first experiments. These included observations on ice, on common air and various forms of 'mephitic' air (air that was unfit for respiration), and on the effect of pressure on the electrification of air in different conditions. He had already brought his history up to the year

1742, but was now held up for lack of source materials, which he shortly expected to receive from other acquaintances in London. Finally, he took the liberty of mentioning that his friends in the north thought it would help the reception of the book if he were admitted to the Royal Society, and that he had written to Watson about this possibility. At the rate he was proceeding he would shortly be able to write up his experiments for presentation to the Society if that would help the application.

Not being particularly skilled in the use of carpentry tools, and not wishing to waste time in making equipment, he called on his brother Timothy (now a Calvinist minister at Manchester) for assistance. Priority was given to a large kite of oiled silk for bringing down electricity from thunder clouds, and Timothy proudly produced it in March. 'It was 6ft 4in wide,' he wrote; 'Joseph could put the whole thing in his pocket, for the frame would take to pieces, and he could walk with it as if he had no more in his hand than a fishing rod.' The string was composed of 36 threads surrounding a metal wire. This was to bring electrical fire from the clouds, Timothy explained; but, he added, 'a philosopher [1] about that time being killed by such an experiment, his wife would not suffer him to raise his heighth'.

By the end of March Priestley was able to send Canton a further instalment of the history for perusal and opinion, and to report that he had carried out several more experiments under Franklin's direction. He had got the kite and would soon have a good apparatus for atmospheric electricity erected 'upon the top of our academy, which is pretty high'. He now asked Canton to obtain various instruments—thermometer, barometer, and hygrometer—suitable for sending up with the kite so that he could record meteorological data at the time of collecting the electricity. Most of the book, he added, had now been written.

Canton, Franklin, Price, and Watson, who had been kept fully informed of his experiments and progress, decided to support him in his desire to join the Royal Society; the nomination was signed also by Samuel Chandler, who had earlier supported the application for the Edinburgh degree. Their recommendation was accurate in every detail.

[1] Professor G. W. Richmann of St Petersburg.

Joseph Priestley of Warrington, Doctor of Laws, author of a chart of Biography, & several other valuable works, a gentleman of great merit & learning, & very well versed in Mathematical & philosophical enquiries, being desirous of offering himself as a candidate for election into this Society, is recomended by us on our personal knowledge, as highly deserving that honour; & we believe that he will, if elected, be a usefull & valuable member.

The election took place on 12 June 1766. Priestley was in London again in August and, with the help of his friends, had completed his task by the end of the year. Even the elegant figures were his own work, for he could not find anyone near at hand to depict apparatus and machines with the accuracy and clarity that he demanded. The book was published in the following autumn and was an immediate success. As the title indicated, it dealt with *The History and Present State of Electricity, with Original Experiments*.

At the end of his *History*, he added a number of queries and hints, as Newton had done before him; but they were not destined to lead to any big advances. The most interesting was one that showed he was already thinking about the age-old problem of the resemblance between the calcination of metals and the respiration processes of plants and animals. It was to occupy him in various ways for the next twenty years. His views on the connection between electricity and chemistry also reveal the cast of his thinking at this time. Both these subjects, he said, have to do with the latent or less obvious properties of bodies; and yet their relation to each other had received little attention and hardly anyone had ever tried to use them together, partly because few electricians were sufficiently well versed in chemistry. Light, he thought with Newton, would prove the key to electrical phenomena 'and other, at present, occult properties of bodies'. Here followed a comment that again foretold the course of his future work. 'Let particular attention be also given to every thing that . . . Natural Philosophy furnishes respecting the Atmosphere, its composition and affections.' He also thought more attention should be given to workshop knowledge—the use of carpentry tools and of the blowpipe for drawing and bending glass tubing. A scientist should be able to construct apparatus according to his needs.

He should not have to rely on the instrument makers, who were seldom men of science and, at that period, aimed mainly at equipment that was elegant and portable. Finally, speaking from experience again, he thought the scientist should be able to depict apparatus according to the rules of perspective, so as to give a clear idea of his experiments to others who might wish to repeat them.

This section was followed with a detailed account of electrical machines and other apparatus, with plenty of good tips on different kinds of machines and batteries, of storage jars and their use. He also dealt with lightning conductors and kites for studying atmospheric electricity, and with precautions to be taken during thunderstorms. To make such portable gear safe, he advocated the use of a trailing chain as an earth. Judging by one cryptic story, such a chain, though increasing the safety of the person flying the kite in the open from an insulated pole, led to the sudden death of at least one neighbour's too-curious goose.

The book ended with an account of his own experiments, written up just as they occurred—failures and successes alike— and as simply as possible. His purpose in adopting this style, which became his normal method of announcing his discoveries, was to show that no superhuman sagacity was required in science and so to encourage others to join in. He realized that this method was 'less calculated to do an author honour as a philosopher', but it would 'contribute more to make other persons philosophers, which is a thing of much more consequence to the public'.

On 4 May 1766 he made a noteworthy discovery, namely that charcoal was an excellent conductor of electricity, and coke an even better one. Though this is the most familiar of Priestley's electrical discoveries, the way in which he came to try the experiment was long overlooked. It shows quite clearly that he was already thinking of the problem that led to some of his greatest work. What alteration does air undergo on passing through a fire or through the lungs, so that it would no longer support the flame of a candle, and how could this vitiated air be restored to its previous wholesomeness?

Having read, and finding by my own experiments, that a candle would not burn in air that had passed through a charcoal fire, or through the lungs of animals, or in any of that air which the chymists call mephitic; I was considering what kind of change it underwent, by passing through the fire, or through the lungs, &c. and whether it was not possible to restore it to its original state, by some operation or mixture. For this purpose, I gave a great degree of intestine motion to it; I threw a quantity of electric matter from the point of a conductor into it, and performed various other operations upon it, but without any effect . . .

He concluded, from some of his own experiments and others reported by David Macbride, that this mephitic air was not anything that had ever been common air, but was 'a fluid *sui generis*', with several properties very different from those of common air. Finding that he could make nothing of mephitic air obtained by passing air through a charcoal fire, he examined charcoal by itself and discovered, as he had suspected, that it was a good conductor. As he was to find soon afterwards, the major problem could not be resolved by electrical means, but only through chemistry. He told Franklin of these experiments before the latter left for the Continent in the summer of 1766. Franklin was reminded of them when he visited the medicinal spring at Pyrmont, which produced enough mephitic air to kill small animals, such as ducks, that attempted to swim on it. More was to be heard of this later.

The simple discovery of charcoal's conducting power has had immense applications, in both science and industry. Priestley went on to say that charcoal (with which he included coke—pit charcoal) was a remarkable substance on other accounts, but it had not been studied properly by any chemist. A thorough examination, he added prophetically, might lead to other important discoveries in chemistry and physics. Meanwhile he had overturned 'one of the earliest and universally received maxims of electricity', namely that water and the metals are conductors, and all other bodies non-conductors. In February he had shown that ice was a good conductor. He then began a course of experiments on 'chymical electricity' and showed that in general all saline substances were good conductors, including solid metallic salts. He also noticed that black-lead in a pencil conducted an electric shock as well as metal or charcoal. These were the original observations which, in the hands of admirers of Priestley's experimental work, such as Volta and Humphry Davy, and other scientists like Faraday and Berzelius, led eventually to an electrical interpretation of chemical reactions.

Priestley also attempted to compare the conductivities of different metals, but in this as in other experiments he was handicapped, as there was no good instrument for measuring electric charges. Here his method was to increase the discharge through a wire of the metal until the metal melted. On 12 November 1766, after many attempts, he succeeded in melting iron wire. Timothy was present at the time and, though a poor writer, he succeeded in conveying something of the excitement that surrounded this work. 'Oh, had Sir Isaac Newton seen such an experiment!' he exclaimed; and Joseph's pleasure on such occasions could not well be described.

Priestley also electrified a hollow metal vessel and found that there was no charge on the inner surface. He inferred that electrical attraction operated according to the same law as gravity, in other words, that the force of attraction between two small charged bodies would vary inversely with the square of the distance between them. Its truth was first demonstrated in 1784–5 by Coulomb, after whom the law is now named.

At this time the study in which Priestley worked at Warrington revealed the remarkable variety of his activities, with materials for his lectures and publications on subjects as diverse as plays and theology, languages and science, history and politics. The young Miss Aikin was very intrigued and amused by it, and left her impressions of it in verse.

> A map of every country known,
> With not a foot of land his own.
> A list of folks that kicked a dust
> On this poor globe, from Ptol. the First;
> He hopes,—indeed it is but fair,—
> Some day to get a corner there.
> A group of all the British kings,
> Fair emblem! on a packthread swings . . .
>
> A shelf of bottles, jar and phial,
> By which the rogues he can defy all,—

All filled with lightning keen and genuine,
And many a little imp he'll pen you in;
Which, like Le Sage's sprite, let out,
Among the neighbours makes a rout;
Brings down the lightning on their houses,
And kills their geese, and frights their spouses!

Then, with reference to his manuscripts, books, and papers, and the publications that soon involved him in bitter controversies, she noticed

A rare thermometer, by which
He settles to the nicest pitch
The just degrees of heat, to raise
Sermons, or politics, or plays.
Papers and books, a strange mixed olio,
From shilling pouch to pompous folio;
Answer, remark, reply, rejoinder,
Fresh from the mint, all stamped and coined here;
Like new-made glass, set by to cool,
Before it bears the workman's tool . . .

Forgotten rhymes and college themes,
Worm-eaten plans and embryo schemes,
A mass of heterogeneous matter,
A chaos dark, nor land nor water;—
New books, like new-born infants, stand,
Waiting the printer's clothing hand;—
Others, a motley ragged brood,
Their limbs unfashioned all, and rude,
Like Cadmus' half-formed men appear . . .

And all, like controversial writing,
Were born with teeth, and sprung up fighting!

Priestley encouraged all the young people about him to practise writing verse, not to make poets of them, but to make them fluent writers of prose. Miss Aikin, indeed, was the most promising of all the versifiers at Warrington. In later years, when Priestley had risen in the world, she remembered these days more wistfully, and in her poem *Characters* she referred to him in these words:

Champion of Truth, alike through Nature's field,
And where in sacred leaves she shines reveal'd,—

Alike in both, eccentric, piercing, bold,
Like his own lightnings, which no chains can hold;
Neglecting caution, and disdaining art,
He seeks no armour for a naked heart:—

Pursue the track thy ardent genius shows,
That like the sun illumines where it goes;
Travel the various map of Science o'er,
Record past wonders, and discover more;
Pour thy free spirit o'er the breathing page,
And wake the virtue of a careless age . . .

Among the friends who interested themselves in Priestley's work generally were Holt, Bentley, and Wedgwood, the last of these occasionally stopping at Warrington to call on him. Thus in 1765 Wedgwood concerned himself in securing notices of the *Essay on Education* in some of the leading journals. In 1766 he followed the electrical experiments with great interest and, in a letter to Bentley in October, he wished Priestley 'all possible success in his delightful and ingenious researches into the secrets of nature'.

This was the most progressive period in the history of the Warrington Academy, and Priestley set the pace. For example, the trustees' report for 1766 was largely occupied with showing the importance of the various courses being provided under his direction. That his fame had spread is undeniable. It is clear, for example, in Jeremy Bentham's account of his tour to the north of England with his father at about the age of sixteen.

'We went to Stockport, Liverpool, Chester, Macclesfield, and the Wiches, where the salt is made. Warrington was then classic ground. Priestley lived there. What would I not have given to have found courage to visit him!' Bentham, the influential writer on parliamentary, municipal, and legal reform, thought he owed his main political maxim to Priestley—that the greatest happiness of the greatest number is the foundation of morals and legislation. Though the actual words do not occur in Priestley's writings, the thought permeated his teaching at Warrington. The idea was not novel in itself, but occurred in Bacon's writings and was a maxim of Roman law. For example, one of the students at Warrington, J. P. Estlin, gave his oration on '*Salus populi suprema lex*. Or an essay to show how far the several forms of government which have been introduced into the world are calculated to promote the happiness of mankind, which is the great end of government.' Such studies were to Priestley one of the two main uses of history. The other he was exemplifying in his scientific work.

Mary Priestley played some part in their next move. She had proved herself to be an excellent housekeeper and organizer; had arranged tea-parties at which the students met their tutor to discuss their work; and had urged and encouraged her husband in everything connected with his career, while relieving him of all domestic cares. She had taken a firm line with students who wished to take too many copies of her husband's lectures, on the ground that they were intended for publication. She had also presented Priestley with a daughter, Sally, who became a family favourite. But Mary's health was delicate and the banks of the Mersey did not suit her. Neither, despite the efforts of the tutors, did the Academy flourish nor succeed in overcoming the hostility and criticism it met from several quarters. For these reasons, rather than any dissatisfaction with the work he was doing, Priestley accepted a call to become minister to a congregation at Mill-Hill Chapel, Leeds, on his home ground. Since his ordination he had moved about considerably and had done a certain amount of preaching, and was now known in Liverpool, Manchester, Bolton, Chowbent, Gateacre, and other places in the region. His call, therefore, was not altogether unexpected, and he moved to Leeds in September 1767.

Chapter 4

Expanding Horizons

PRIESTLEY spent almost six years at Leeds, without doubt some of the most vigorous, productive, and strenuous years of his life. We cannot gloss over them, for they saw him at his best—in his late thirties—full of reforming zeal and with an ardent desire to serve his fellow men. It was the period in which he gained the reputation of being the most assiduous 'bookmaker' of his generation, for he produced more than a score of original publications during that time. They varied from theological, political, and scientific pamphlets to works of one, two, and three volumes on a number of subjects. He could not have done all this without the mass of manuscripts he brought with him from Warrington; nor would he have done so much had not certain unpleasing turns in public affairs made him determined 'to stick out his neck', as he put it to Mrs Barbauld.

This led him into a great deal of unexpected and largely unwelcome argument, so much so that by 1770 he expressed the hope that he had 'quite done with controversy'; but this was not to be. By that time he had irrevocably taken the stand in religion and politics to which he remained steadfast to the end of his days, and which, more than anything else, determined the course of his future career. It was also the period of some of his best scientific work, and it will be no discredit to his reputation in this field to sketch first the background against which this work was done.

Priestley now ministered to a larger and more influential congregation than any he had been connected with before, and he spared no effort to serve them well. But his duties took up only a few hours of his waking life. The rest of them he spent in his customary methodical and industrious manner. As an educationist he retained his interest in the academies, and regarded teaching and preaching as complementary. Though he had no school, he aroused sufficient support to found a successful public-subscription library, as had Bentley and others at Liverpool. He was careful to instruct the young among his congregation, and arranged them in three separate groups—children under 14 for catechizing, older children for Bible study, and young men for instructing in the principles of dissent. For the children he had produced a catechism adapted from the earlier one of Isaac Watts; it had already reached its second edition in 1767, and was still being printed in its ninth edition after the Napoleonic Wars.

Priestley's *Essay on Education* appeared again in London in 1768. In response to a strong demand, he wrote a *Familiar Introduction to Electricity* for beginners; it was quickly bought up on its appearance in 1768 and a second edition was required in the following year. His *History of Electricity* had been well received, and he issued additions to this as well as a second edition in 1769. He also completed his *Description of a Chart of History*, which he had begun at Warrington, and printed it in 1769; this reached its fifteenth edition in 1816. As for some time there had been no useful account of the art of drawing, which was much neglected, he also prepared a *Familiar Introduction to Perspective*, which was printed in 1770 and was generally liked. In all this work he adapted himself easily to different audiences—the very young who had scarcely learned to read, the student able to grasp anything properly explained, the educationist, and the scientist. For Priestley it was enough to know that he was being useful to mankind. He thought nothing of the astonishment his varied activities were creating, or of the criticism he began to receive for trying to bring science down to the level of the average reader. In truth these works were only a small part of his total effort, for he was planning even more ambitious tasks.

Though it would be out of place here to discuss his theological work in any detail, one book must be mentioned—the *Institutes of Natural and Revealed Religion*—for it explains much of his outlook, and it played an important part, not only in the Unitarian movement, but also in the attacks that eventually drove him from England.

4

He already had a reputation for fearless criticism. He believed, for example, that many of the arguments advanced by Paul in his letters to the early Christians were faulty, and he said so. He thought that some of the explanations of diseases given in the New Testament were no longer tenable, and he said so. In his *Institutes* he wrote about early religions and their impact on the thought of the Christian church, and suddenly made the bold deduction that seemed to him to follow from the evidence. He thought that official Christendom had deified a man, and he said that plainly too. Even today the passage almost stands out from the page.

Upon the very same principles, and in the very same manner, by which dead men came to be worshipped by the ancient idolaters, there was introduced into the christian church, in the first place, the idolatrous worship of Jesus Christ, then that of the Virgin Mary, and lastly that of innumerable other saints, and of angels also; and this modern christian idolatry has been attended with all the absurdities, and with some, but not all the immoralities, of the ancient heathen idolatry. It has, however, evidently promoted a very great neglect of the duties we owe both to God and man.

This work contained the instruction he gave to the young men of the congregation at Mill-Hill, and it had grown from the first draft he made at Daventry into three volumes, which were published one a year from 1772 to 1774. An account of all the 'corruptions' that had occurred since the first days of Christianity was to have been a fourth volume, but it became too large to include in the series, and was published separately.

Priestley's critics were right in seeing here a threat to the Established Church and a calculated attempt to lead the young away from it and to eschew the doctrine of the Trinity. The Reformation had been a good thing, he taught, but it had not gone far enough. Many so-called Christian teachings were incompatible with other kinds of truth, such as those being discovered daily by science. The corruptions that had been introduced into Christianity since its early days must, he maintained, be eradicated from it, or the Church would flounder. This could be done by applying the well-known and well-tried methods of discovering truth—methods that were nowhere more clearly shown than in the writings of Locke, Hartley, and

Newton. He thought, however, that sudden changes were unnecessary and undesirable.

At the beginning of the book he summarized his advice to the young as follows:

> Above all things, be careful to improve and make use of the *reason* which God has given you, to be the guide of your lives, to check the extravagance of your passions, and to assist you in acquiring that knowledge, without which your rational powers will be of no advantage to you . . . have nothing to do with a parliamentary religion, or a parliamentary God.

This was strong meat, as even his friends realized. It was an open invitation to the young to examine the beliefs of their fathers, to look closely at the connection between Church and State, and consequently to scrutinize the Constitution and the rights of the King himself. It is easy to see how such teachings appeared as a threat to Anglicans. But they also displeased many Dissenters, who generally resented too close an inquiry into the very roots of their religious beliefs; nor did they welcome any innovations likely to rouse the Church and the Government, whose lethargy did at least ensure to them a measure of security; for there were still penal laws that made it possible for the Crown to punish severely any who refused to subscribe to the 39 Articles. But it was already too late for any such considerations to count with him; he had already started —in Mrs Barbauld's phrase—to 'wake the virtue of a careless age'.

This process had begun at Warrington in his writings on education and his lectures on history, and his important new *Essay on the First Principles of Government* was developed directly from them. This was published in London and Dublin in 1768 and was one of his best literary works, addressed to thinking people of all descriptions. It was no timid composition from a meek dissenting preacher in the provinces, but the mature thinking of a cultivated man who made no apology for 'writing with the freedom becoming a philosopher, a man, and an Englishman'. He spoke the language of no party, and owed allegiance to none. His approach was unusual, but he developed his theme with great clarity and force, and his conclusions were just.

It requires but a few years to comprehend the whole preceding progress of any one art or science; and the rest of a man's life, in which his faculties are the most perfect, may be given to the extension of it.

Here spoke the historian and the historian of science. Since all knowledge was power, as Bacon observed, human powers would increase as the materials and the laws of Nature were brought more and more under man's command; 'men will make their situation in this world abundantly more easy and comfortable; they will probably prolong their existence in it, and will grow daily more happy . . .'.

One of Priestley's innovations was to distinguish between political and civil liberty. True political liberty existed only in those societies where every member enjoyed an equal opportunity of arriving at the highest offices; but at that time no society on earth had ever been formed on such a pattern. From this he developed the viewpoint that was characteristic of early liberal thought:

It must necessarily be understood, therefore, that all people live in society for their mutual advantage; so that the good and happiness of the members, that is the majority of the members of any state, is the great standard by which every thing relating to that state must finally be determined.

Priestley could not understand why this great object of all government, as he called it, had been so little understood or insisted upon by writers in the past; for 'this one general idea, properly pursued, throws the greatest light upon the whole system of policy, morals, and, I may add, theology too'. It was a fundamental maxim, also, that kings, senators, and nobles enjoyed their ranks and privileges because the good of the State required it. To all intents and purposes they were servants of the public and accountable to the people. He reminded his readers that there were such things as principles of revolutionary activity, and he outlined the basis on which such activity could be justified. Here he became eloquent and, most unusually, indulged himself with a sentence of 223 words in the tradition of classical orators. It could be clearly seen from this in which countries he thought a revolution would be justified, but it was equally clear that such activity could not be justified in England. The Glorious Revolution of 1688 had seen to it once for all. 'God be thanked, the government of this country is now fixed upon so good and firm a basis, and is so generally acquiesced in, that they are only the mere tools of a court party, or the narrow minded bigots among the inferior clergy, who, to serve their own low purposes, do now and then promote the cry, that the church or the state is in danger.'

But the government of that day, he justly maintained, was no fit body to be entrusted with matters that involved the exercise of private conscience. This applied particularly to religion and education. The art of education, he pointed out, was in its infancy, and in that state of its growth it would be stifled if put into the hands of the civil magistrate. Far more experiment was still necessary. Variety was characteristic of human nature, uniformity of the brute creation. He preferred the Athenians to the Spartans.

Priestley made it clear, too, that he would strongly deprecate any attempt to overthrow all the ecclesiastical establishments in Europe, for this would be too hazardous. 'Reform them first, do not throw them aside entirely until experience shows no good can be made of them.'

As regards Great Britain, his suggestions were fundamental enough, but at least two bishops agreed substantially with him:

(1) Reduce the number of Articles from 39 to 1; it was sufficient for anyone to believe in the religion of Jesus Christ, as set forth in the New Testament;

(2) Let the livings of the clergy be made more equal, in proportion to the duties expected of them;

(3) Let the clergy be confined to ecclesiastical duty and have nothing to do in conducting the affairs of state; their presence in the cabinet could be dangerous;

(4) Every member of the community should enjoy every right of a citizen, whether he conformed to the Church of England or not. If he had sufficient ability, he should be considered qualified to serve his country in any civil capacity.

Already, he pointed out, a popish country like Poland showed more toleration than this country. France, he said, could be expected to follow and improve on Poland's example. If

England did not quickly improve the state of its liberties dire results might follow, for 'that great and indefatigable rival power [France], by one master stroke of policy, may almost depopulate this great and flourishing kingdom'.

It was often thought that changes of the kind he wished to see could be introduced only by violent measures. 'I would endeavour to stop the ablest hand that should attempt to reform in this manner; because it is hardly possible but that a remedy so effected must be worse than the disease.' History need not always repeat itself, but it was a fact that every body of men, with the sole exception of the Quakers, had in the past turned persecutors when they had power.

This, in substance, was the stand Priestley took and which he enlarged upon in a number of tracts and a few anonymous pamphlets, in which he had the help not only of his religious friends but also, on occasion, of Franklin and John Wilkes. This was the cause of some thirty years of vituperation that formed a cacophonous background to Priestley's scientific work. Though once or twice in later years he became almost distracted by the mounting opposition to his views, he never lacked the support of staunch friends. Nor did he budge from his principles, but from time to time emerged with forthright pamphlets, some of which drove his opponents to utter exasperation.

Priestley did not expect to see all his ideals become realities during his lifetime, and some of his thoughts he left for the consideration of 'future ages'. But his whole outlook was summed up in his clarion call in the *First Principles of Government*:

Let all the friends of liberty and human nature join to free the minds of men from the shackles of narrow and impolitic laws. Let us be free ourselves, and leave the blessings of freedom to our posterity.

That so little of this sounds offensive to modern ears shows that Priestley was in the van of progress towards a freer and more tolerant England. But several churchmen tried to answer him, to demonstrate the supremacy of the Anglican establishment, and to remind the people that all other sects were illegal. A direct answer to Priestley was given early in 1769 by the

Archdeacon of Winchester at the consecration of Johnathan Shipley (brother of William Shipley, a founder of the Society of Arts) as Bishop of Llandaff, his text being: 'Obey them that have the rule over you, and submit yourselves.' Some of the arguments brought forward against nonconformity reveal the pernicious ideas that Priestley was combating. If the Church once relaxed, said the Archdeacon, the time would come when every sect whose principles were not clearly inconsistent with good government would call for toleration. Such views gave Priestley a good starting-point for carefully reasoned answers. On this occasion he replied with a text: 'In vain do they worship me, teaching for doctrines the commandments of men.' He hoped that such arguments for church authority would soon be 'consigned to everlasting oblivion, as the disgrace of human reason, and human nature'.

At this time also William Blackstone's celebrated *Commentaries on the Laws of England* were being published, and in the fourth volume he made some strong attacks on the Dissenters. His tendency to think that any change in one part of the law would upset the whole structure brought a quick and equally vigorous retort from Priestley, and, at other times, from Bentham and the mysterious writer ' Junius'. Priestley dealt summarily with the arguments Blackstone adduced from statutes that had never been repealed, such as those of Edward VI and Elizabeth I, which made confiscation of goods and imprisonment for life the punishment for saying anything derogatory about the book of common prayer. He said that Blackstone's best argument had been that any alteration in the constitution or liturgy of the Church of England would endanger the union between England and Scotland, but proceeded to dismiss the idea as absurd.

Priestley then suggested that Blackstone should alter some of his remarks about Dissenters in the next edition of his book. For example, instead of referring to the 'virulent declamations of peevish and opinionated men' he should write 'the calm reasonings of sober and conscientious men'.

There seems no doubt that Priestley had the better of both antagonists. Blackstone, in his reply, said he would alter some of his passages, but he warned Priestley that nonconformity was still a crime according to the laws of England.

These are some of the reasons why Priestley's stay at Leeds was so eventful, not only to his congregation alone, but for a much wider public. We have yet to consider the large amount of scientific work he carried out there at the same time, work of great importance in the history of science, and especially of chemistry. Did Leeds soon forget him? We may doubt this, for his congregation chose William Wood, another man of public spirit and scientific interests, as his successor. And it was no mere fanciful whim that caused Wood, when the news of Priestley's death reached Leeds thirty-two years later, to preach from the text: 'He was a burning and a shining light; and ye were willing for a season to rejoice in his light.'

Chapter 5

Electricity, Light, and Air

WHEN Priestley arrived at Leeds, he found that the minister's house in Basinghall Street was not ready for him, and so he was obliged to make a temporary home in Meadow Lane, next to the public brewery of Jakes and Nell. This meant the postponement of his plan to set up a proper laboratory for experiments. In the meantime, however, he could carry on with his work in electricity and associated questions connected with light and the atmosphere. It was also possible to continue the study of astronomy, for which some instruments but not a laboratory were required. Timothy said that when Joseph began to study astronomy, he took books and papers into the fields, and, as few people then knew much about the subject, this helped to spread his reputation as a man of science.

One of his major preoccupations was the design of a simple and cheap electrical machine suitable for those taking up electricity for the first time. He decided upon a light high-geared machine standing on three feet, weighted with lead or screwed to the floor, this last being desirable to prevent it from moving about when the handle was turned vigorously. 'Tim', who was in great need of extra income for his growing family, and was good with a lathe and other tools, turned the legs and the stand, and saw to the brass-work, which was done for them locally. ' Jo', who was deft with his fingers but less expert with tools, helped to assemble them. These new machines were described fully in the second edition of the *History* (*see* Plate 7), and the brothers made several for sale to friends and other interested inquirers.

The main purpose of this design was to ensure that the frame, wheel, rotating globe, rubber, and prime conductor were all separable and adjustable.

The frame, which supported the wheel and the spindle carrying the rotating globe, was made of two strong boards of mahogany. The rubber was made of a hollow piece of copper filled with horse-hair and covered with a 'basil skin' (tanned sheepskin), and it was insulated by a plate of glass.

The prime conductor was a pear-shaped hollow vessel of copper, which received its electric charge through a long bent wire or a rod of very soft brass, with an open ring at its end in which a number of sharply pointed wires were held. These were allowed to play lightly on the globe as it turned. The main body of the conductor had several holes in which metallic rods could be inserted in order to charge them.

One such machine was supplied for medical purposes to the Leeds Infirmary, for whose support collections were sometimes taken at Mill-Hill. The surgeon there, William Hey (later F.R.S.), was on friendly terms with Priestley. In December 1769 the Quarterly Board ordered 'That Mr. Hey be desired to procure an Electrical Machine of Dr. Priestley's newest Construction for the use of this Charity'. It cost £5 11s 6d and was still in use in July 1790, when Hey was requested to superintend its repair.[1] At that time electric shocks were often administered for the treatment of some nervous disorders. John Wesley wrote about such uses of electricity, and the press often carried accounts of remarkable cures.

Priestley still kept up his practice of spending the early part of each year in London, renewing and extending his acquaintance with men of diverse interests, dining at clubs, occasionally preaching for his friend Price, attending meetings of the Royal Society, and at times reading papers on his electrical and chemical researches. Thus additional experiments, and earlier ones not fully described in his *History*, were discussed in papers read during March 1768, February and March 1769, and March and April 1770. In the first of these he showed the assembled Fellows a number of metal plates on which electric discharges had taken place from a conductor brought close to them. These plates were marked with a number of concentric areas, each having all the colours of the spectrum. When he showed them to Canton, he was informed that a similar effect

[1] Information kindly supplied by Dr S. T. Anning of Leeds.

had been noticed when a discharge took place through any fine metal wire stretched over a piece of glass. Priestley thought these patterns resembled Newton's rings somewhat, and that they were caused by heat on the surface of the metal, the colour depending on the thickness of the metal affected.

In the following year he described work to do with the force of electrical 'explosions', and found that light objects were scattered by an electric discharge nearby, though they did not acquire any charge from it.

In 1770 he gave a full account of his experiments with charcoal, and described a new phenomenon, which he called the 'lateral explosion', but which later became known as the side-flash. Priestley (like some others) had noticed that when Leyden jars were discharged a slight shock was sometimes felt, although his body was not in the circuit. To see whether electricity could in fact pass from a circuit to neighbouring objects, he covered a long pasteboard tube with metal foil and suspended it about $\frac{1}{4}$ inch away from a metal rod connected to the outside of the battery. On discharging the battery he saw a spark pass from the rod to the insulated tube, but the tube did not acquire any charge. He repeated this more than fifty times to be sure of the result and then carried out a similar experiment in a vacuum, using a second metal rod in place of the tube. When the rods were brought to within 2 inches of each other, a 'thin blue or purple light' bridged the gap. In ordinary sparks, he said, the electrical matter rushed in one direction only, but here it went across the gap and returned in the same path. This seems to have been the first observation and recognition of an oscillatory discharge. The phenomenon was studied independently by several workers in the nineteenth century. In the hands of Hertz, Oliver Lodge (who still used Leyden jars), and others, the study of oscillatory discharges was greatly extended; Rutherford and Marconi in turn developed their discoveries for signalling purposes, and so initiated the age of radio and television. But for a long period Priestley's work remained an isolated and little understood episode in the history of electricity.

Though this was the last important piece of work he carried out as an electrician separately from his chemical studies, we

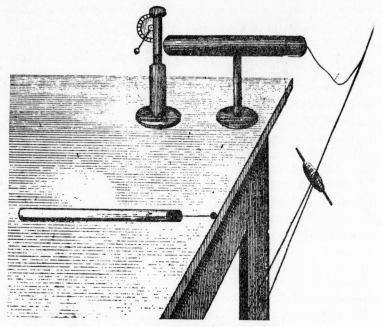

Fig. 1 Henley's electrometer (*left*) being used with a prime conductor
connected to the conducting string of a kite. (After Cavallo)

cannot leave the subject without pointing to the great deal of
interest his books had created among the reading public and
young people, several of whom became electricians as a result.
Of these, special mention should be made of William Henley
(or Henly) of Southwark and his friend Tiberius Cavallo. In
October 1770 Priestley was busy writing up a report of work
sent to him by Henley and Thomas Ronayne of Cork.[1] This
was sent in the form of a letter to Franklin, for onward trans-
mission to the Royal Society. Henley's work was considered of
importance and was published in the *Philosophical Transactions*
for 1771. In his *History* Priestley had said that a good electrometer was one of the great desiderata, and Henley set out to
supply one. His instrument (Fig. 1) had a main stem of box-
wood or ivory that could be screwed into the prime conductor
of an electrical machine or into the knob of a Leyden jar; the

[1] They had already been working in the field (see e.g. British Museum, Add.
MS. 4439, Ronayne to T. Birch, 20 July 1762).

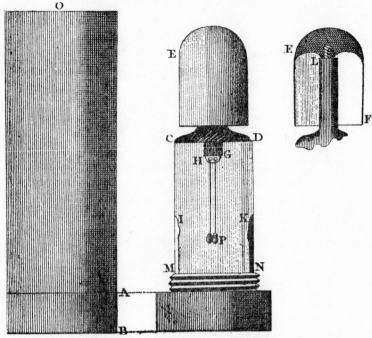

Fig. 2 Cavallo's electrometer, according to a design suggested to him by Ronayne.

measuring part of the device was a small cork ball suspended by a light rod from the centre of a semicircle graduated like a protractor. With this he attempted to improve on Priestley's comparison of the conducting powers of metals by noting the movement of the rod on the scale caused by a charge sufficient to melt an inch of wire of the metal in the circuit. Henley also suggested an improvement of Canton's pithball electroscope. Cavallo made a number of others, and also invented an electrometer (Fig. 2) which came into general use. This consisted of two pieces of cork suspended by silver wires, which were connected by a further insulated wire to a brass cap.

Alessandro Volta was another man who corresponded with Priestley in a similar manner. Volta, among other things, invented the electrophorus, an instrument for storing electricity and used for transferring charges as required to other conductors (Fig. 3). Though Priestley could claim none of the

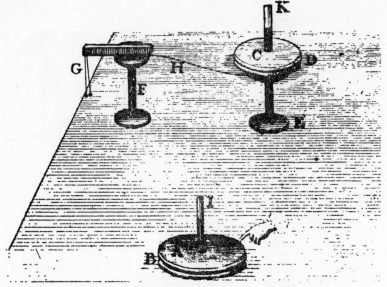

Fig. 3 Volta's electrophorus for transferring electric charges. (After Cavallo)

credit for subsequent discoveries, he gave an impetus to the subject, and was justified in viewing them with a paternal interest, considering them 'to some extent' as the result of his own work.

By the spring of 1770 Priestley had formed an ambitious plan to write a history of the whole of experimental philosophy, though he had previously said that this was too difficult a task for one man. Thus he now regarded the history of electricity as the first volume of a comprehensive series. On his annual visit to London he dropped the hint to some of his colleagues, and they tried to enlist the help of a patron to defray his expenses, which he estimated at £200 to £300 for books alone, much more than he could himself afford in view of his family responsibilities. His friends sounded the Duke of Northumberland, formerly Sir Hugh Smithson, who was sufficiently interested to ask for a plan of the work. Priestley immediately wrote a short outline of his project, as follows:

Dr. Priestley having written the *History and Present State of Electricity*, would willingly undertake to write the history of all the other branches of *experimental philosophy* upon the same extensive plan. He apprehends that a work of this kind exhibiting a view of all that has been done already, would, on several accounts greatly facilitate future discoveries in science; but he has hitherto been discouraged from undertaking it by the expenses in which it would necessarily involve him, and which he is not able to supply; particularly in procuring the books to which he cannot have access in his present situation . . .

He went on to explain that he would have to enlarge his stock of apparatus in order to settle disputed points and to carry out further experiments that would no doubt occur to him as he went along. His work on electricity had well repaid his efforts in this way. He concluded: 'Dr. Priestley would think himself greatly honoured, if his Grace the Duke of Northumberland should think this work worthy of his patronage.'

By the end of May 1770 he was busier than ever in composing and transcribing from shorthand: 'I have frequently written until I could hardly hold the pen; for writing long hand is irksome, and, indeed, painful to me.' He had made a similar comment when writing to Canton from Warrington, and it seems, as he said on a later occasion, that he suffered periodically from rheumatism.

By the end of July he had received practical help in the form of books. A large hamper had arrived 'from a person unknown', who, it transpired, was Sir George Savile, one of the two county Members of Parliament for Yorkshire, and the most respected politician of the day. The Duke of Northumberland had also sent him some books from his library; they included the large French *Encyclopédie*, which unfortunately was of little use, as Priestley was looking for accounts of actual experiments written at first hand.

Meanwhile he enlisted the help of Theophilus Lindsey, a clergyman at Catterick, Yorkshire, whom he had met when on a visit to the somewhat heterodox Archdeacon of Cleveland, Francis Blackburne, whose son was at Warrington. Lindsey, who was dissatisfied with the Church, resigned his living, and subsequently became Priestley's most intimate friend and minister of the first Unitarian chapel—in Essex Street off the Strand. In early August, Lindsey, who was acquainted with the Duke, found an opportunity to see him and to recommend Priestley's proposal, telling him what progress had already been made.

This was the time when Priestley hoped he had finished with controversy, for he was devoting six hours a day to the collection of materials for his great work—as he was beginning to think of it—and had calculated that at this rate he would 'do a good deal of business' in six years. With his industry there seems little doubt that he could have completed what he set out to do. But no financial support came and he had already spent £100 on books. By November he had decided to write up first the history of discoveries relating to light and colours and to judge by its reception as to whether any further volumes should be produced. With the aid of book-lists circulated with his printed proposals, many works that were difficult to find had been made available to him, including scientific papers from Sweden, which apparently were obtained in translation by Savile from his mother's physician, William Lewis.

By December Priestley had concluded, from the lack of financial support, that he had better print the book by subscription to make sure of recovering his expenses. By the end of the year the book was almost finished, and he was well satisfied with it. He found that light was a fine subject for the historian, much better, in fact, than electricity. A large number of plates would be required, he said, and the general effect should be pleasing. He thought it was as much needed as the former history, for few even of his scientific friends had much idea of how discoveries in optics had taken place. But public taste, he realized, was capricious, and if the book was not well received he would go no further.

During the early months of 1771 the subscription list grew satisfactorily and it was decided to print. The list of subscribers gives a very good idea of his extensive acquaintance, for a large number of them occur from time to time in his correspondence and writings or are mentioned as friends. There were many Fellows of the Royal Society and several merchants. Franklin took twenty copies, presumably for his friends in America. The Vaughan family, with whom he was acquainted from his Warrington days, took seven copies, John Lee five, and Savile

Plate 5 Joseph Priestley, *c.* 1765. The 'Leeds' portrait, now in the possession of the Royal Society. (*By permission of the Council*)

Plate 6 Priestley's greatest patron, the Earl of Shelburne, Baron Wycombe (later 1st Marquis of Lansdowne). When Prime Minister in 1782–3, Shelburne negotiated the treaty with the American colonies. He was buried in the Parish Church, High Wycombe. (*National Portrait Gallery*)

three. Bentley and Wedgwood subscribed. Politicians sympathetic to his work included the Marquis of Rockingham,[1] Edmund Burke, William Eden (later Earl of Auckland), the Hon. Charles James Fox, and John Wilkes. Joseph Priestley of Halifax, who took an active interest in Yorkshire politics, and John Priestley of Fieldhead appear, together with noted teachers of science, such as Arden of Beverley, Nicholson of Wakefield, and the celebrated Adam Walker. Several academies, acquaintances in the University of Cambridge, and well-known names in the history of science and medicine are there too. The Duke of Northumberland, whom Priestley visited in London, received him kindly and accepted the suggestion that the first volume should be dedicated to him.

The production of the book must have seemed very slow to Priestley, for it was not ready until the beginning of 1772. From the dedication it is clear that he had not yet given up hope of seeing the whole project through, as he called it the first volume of *The History of all the Branches of Experimental Philosophy*. His printed proposals had indicated that the next subject would be magnetism; but there now seemed two possibilities, he said, and he proposed to wait some time to see whether it would be worth his while to continue in this way. If it seemed doubtful he would devote himself instead to the history of discoveries relating to air. He announced that he had been engaged in a course of experiments on phenomena of vegetation and respiration, and had given special attention to the noxious kinds of air, such as fixed air, various kinds of inflammable air, air affected with the breath of animals or putrid matter, and so on. Priestley was certainly a man who believed that the labourer is worthy of his hire. Immortality, he said, was not a sufficient reward for works like these.

In his *History and Present State of Discoveries relating to Vision, Light, and Colours* Priestley gave very clear descriptions of the development of various branches of the subject and adopted a critical attitude. Thus he took great pleasure in writing about Newton's discoveries, although, as others had done, he criticized

---

[1] For Rockingham's interests, see W. H. G. Armytage, *Notes & Records*, 1957, *12*, 64.

Newton's explanations of the phenomenon known as Newton's rings and R. J. Boscovich's attempts to explain the rainbow. Throughout he added constructive hints for those wishing to follow up the experimental side of the subject and tried to comment usefully on controversial issues.

Being interested in anatomy and in Hartley's views on man, he paid special attention to 'the proper seat of vision', taking advantage of Hey's position in the Infirmary to obtain direct information about the eye and its diseased conditions. As a result he became fully convinced that the retina was the centre where visual images are registered, and that these images are in turn transferred to the brain via the optic nerve.

That the optic nerve is of principal use in vision is farther probable from several phenomena attending some of the diseases in which the sight is affected. When an amaurosis has affected one eye only, the optic nerve of that eye has been found manifestly altered from its sound state. I myself was present when Mr. Hey examined the brain of a young girl, who had been blind of one eye, and saw that the optic nerve belonging to it was considerably smaller than the other; and he informed me that, upon cutting into it, he found it to be much harder, and cinericious.

Several other arguments of an anatomical nature were added.

He gave a full account of optical instruments, including Kircher's magic lantern, one of the things he afterwards kept by him for the amusement of the children; for during his stay at Leeds two sons, Joseph and William, were born. Small coloured figures were painted on glass, and the greatly magnified images were viewed on a screen or whitened wall. Another instrument he had found of great interest to the young pupils at his school in Nantwich was Lieberkühn's solar microscope, invented in 1738–9 and made after that time by Cuff in Fleet Street, London. A beam of sunlight was reflected by a mirror into a tube containing a movable convex lens, the whole being attached to a Wilson's microscope, and inserted in a hole in a shutter of a darkened room. Greatly magnified images of small objects mounted on a glass slide could then be thrown on to a white screen.

Priestley acknowledged his considerable debt to the Rev. John Michell, of Thornhill, whom he called his friend and neighbour, and who is best known as the inventor of the torsion balance. In some of the more interesting parts of the history, indeed, Priestley discussed matters on which he had Michell's advice, or described experiments of Michell's which had been explained to him in person. One of the main questions of the day was the nature of light. Did it consist of particles or of waves? Michell had tried out an experiment with a sheet of copper delicately supported and able to turn by being attached to an agate cup placed over a needle-point. He found that the vane revolved when sunlight fell on one half of it from a 2-foot concave mirror. From the speed of the movement the 'momentum' of the light was calculated. This made it possible to work out the weight that could be presumed to have been lost by the sun since the creation! Assuming that the sun had a density about that of water, they concluded that the radius of the sun had decreased by about ten feet. Later, when light had come to be regarded as electromagnetic radiation, and of the same fundamental nature as matter, it was realized that light would in any event exert a very small pressure on bodies, but in Michell's experiments the movement resulted from the irregular heating of the vane.

One of the unexpected results of Priestley's studies of light and of optical and astronomical instruments was an invitation to join Captain James Cook's second voyage of scientific discovery as the expedition's astronomer. The invitation came to him through his friends William Eden and John Lee towards the end of 1771. Priestley at first hesitated, not for any thought for himself, but only to make sure that it would not be to his family's disadvantage.

No person can have a more domestic turn than myself, or be more happy in his family connections. I shall leave an affectionate wife, and three children, at an age which is, of all others, the most engaging.

But, he added, the ardour he felt for the promotion of natural knowledge would induce him to leave them for a time. When, in his *History of Electricity*, he had referred with enthusiasm to these expeditions of discovery, he little thought he would ever have an opportunity to take part in one of them. He had now

finished the book on light and could devote himself to preparing for his work on the voyage.

But Priestley did not yet know the power of the forces he had
aroused against himself—forces that could override the wishes
of his colleagues in the Royal Society and in government circles,
or even cancel what appeared to be official invitations. He had
already accepted when Joseph Banks, then in charge of the
scientific arrangements, informed him that 'some clergymen in
the Board of Longitude, who had the direction of this business',
had objected to his appointment because of his religious
principles.

As Priestley was able to smile at this, we may too. Yet there
was a more serious side, for at that time there were movements
afoot to obtain some relaxation of the laws relating to religious
tests. But George III was taking a personal stand against them,
and had issued what amounted to a direction to Lord North,
the leader of the government, to oppose any such measures in
the House of Commons. If by any chance the Commons failed
in their 'duty', the King would see to it that 'mischief' was
prevented when any such bill reached the Lords. This he did
on occasion by acting as his own Whip. On 23 February 1772,
in a letter addressed to Lord North, he put his point of view
forcibly: [1]

I own myself . . . a great enemy to any innovations, for, in this
mixed government it is highly necessary to avoid novelties . . . I am
sorry to say the present Presbyterians seem so much more resembling
Socinians than Christians, that I think the test was never so necessary
as at present for obliging them to prove themselves Christians.

By proclaiming himself a Socinian (or Unitarian), Priestley
was henceforth to be regarded officially as an enemy of the
court, and not even a Christian. From a later letter to North,
it is clear that the King thought it within his right even to
disapprove of Eden's friendship with Priestley, although they
had common interests. Eden had translated the Marquis of
Beccaria's *Essay on Crimes and Punishments*, which Priestley was
one of the first to comment upon, and had recently completed
a book on *Principles of Penal Law*.

[1] B. Dobrée (Ed.), *The Letters of King George III*, London, 1935, 82.

Priestley had so many other useful things to do that he scarcely minded the rebuff. Indeed, he tried to make a useful contribution to the expedition, in the form of a drink that might help to prevent scurvy.

This arose from his interest in mephitic air, and the fact that he had lived for a time near a brewery. He had not been there long before he realized that there was a permanent and plentiful supply of mephitic air (Joseph Black's 'fixed air') above the fermenting liquor in the vats. Very soon Priestley and the workmen were carrying out simple experiments with candles, burning chips of wood, and red-hot pokers. Smoke from the wood stayed in the fixed air, and, if swirled around, it could be seen to fall over the side of the vat and down to the floor, showing that it was heavier than the outside air. When water was placed in a shallow dish over the vat it acquired a pleasant, acidulous taste that reminded him of the Pyrmont and Seltzer mineral waters. Soon he found that this could be done in 2 to 3 minutes by pouring water continuously from one vessel to another near the top of the vat. The fixed air had dissolved in the water to give what was eventually known as soda-water. He gave some of this water to his friends, including John Lee, at the end of 1767 and early in 1768. But not all the experiments worked out so well. He appears to have desisted after trying to find out if ether would dissolve fixed air. The ether kept bubbling, the vapour escaped, and the result was that the whole of that particular brew was spoilt.

He had almost forgotten about this by the early spring of 1772, when he was in London and was invited to dine with the Duke of Northumberland. On that occasion the Duke produced a bottle of distilled water that had been made by Charles Irving, a naval surgeon, as suitable for use in ships on long voyages. It was wholesome, but flat, and unlikely to be appreciated by seamen. Priestley immediately remembered his earlier experiments, and thought how easy it would be to make the water pleasant and at the same time give the navy an additional weapon against scurvy; for Macbride, as well as many physicians among his own acquaintance, including James Lind,[1]

---

[1] For the part played by Jame Lind, see L. H. Roddis, *James Lind . . .*, London, 1951, pp. 95, 102, 144.

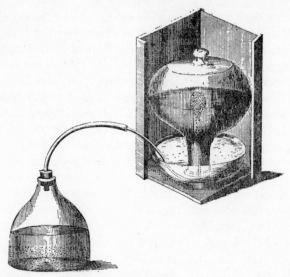

Fig. 4 Quick method for impregnating water with fixed air. The earlier method is shown in Plate 9.

were of the opinion that fixed air might have this useful property. Priestley mentioned this to the Duke and to the company, who all seemed very pleased with the idea.

The next day he got together a small apparatus in his lodgings —made up from vessels in constant use by the family—and 'impregnated' some of the domestic water (supplied from the New River) until it had absorbed about its own volume of fixed air (*see* Fig. 4 and Plate 9). The operation was completed in about half an hour. A few days later, having been invited to call on his other patron, Sir George Savile, he took with him a bottle of the water and explained his object in preparing it. Savile insisted there and then on writing a card to Lord Sandwich, who said he would be glad to see them the next day. Accordingly Priestley drew up a short statement of his proposal, and Sandwich promised to submit it to the Lords Commissioners of the Admiralty. They considered the suggestion on 1 April, and decided to have experiments made with it on certain warships, provided they were first satisfied that 'the Water medicated as aforesaid shall be free from any noxious qualities'. A letter was sent to the President of the College of Physicians asking that the gentlemen of the College would 'confer with Dr. Priestley, with respect to his Process (he being desired to attend them for that purpose) and favour their Lordships with their opinion whether the Water produced thereby is wholesome and fit to be made use of for drinking . . .'.

Throughout April, Irving's distillation apparatus, which had been given preliminary trials in the previous autumn, was tested on several more ships. For example, the *Terrible* was ordered to try out the process 'upon one Beef day, one Pork day and at least one Banyan [that is, meatless] day'. Samples of the distilled water were sent to their Lordships daily.

Captain Cook's vessels, the *Resolution* and the *Adventure*, were lying at anchor in Longreach, being fitted and taking in supplies. One of the purposes of the voyage was to test special foods reputed to prevent scurvy, and among these were 'marmalade of carrots', 'rob of oranges and lemons', and 'inspissated juice of malt'. Priestley's impregnated water, it was decided, would usefully supplement these special foods.

Meanwhile Priestley had returned to Leeds, and he must have been very gratified to receive, on 2 May, a letter informing him that the Lords of the Admiralty had ordered the *Resolution* and the *Adventure*

> to make Experiments & observations from time to time in the course of their intended Voyage of your proposed method for the improvement of Water used at Sea & more particularly Water distilled from Sea Water by impregnating the same with fixed Air; I am commanded by their Lordships to acquaint you therewith & desire you will please to communicate your process to the Commanders of the said Sloops, and furnish the Surgeons of them with the necessary instructions for the preparation & use of the impregnated Water accordingly.

Priestley prepared his directions and forwarded them on 7 May, and he learnt a few days later that they had reached the sloops' commanders. On 16 May it was ordered that Irving's apparatus should be fitted to 'both Coppers in each of His Majesty's Sloops the Resolution and Adventure' and spare condenser tubes were also supplied.[1]

[1] Public Records Office, ADM 2/546, under 11 and 13 March; 1, 7, 20 April; 1, 2, 16, 28 May; also ADM 2/731, under 1, 11, 28 April; 13 and 27 May.

In the same month the printing of Priestley's *Directions for impregnating water with fixed air, in order to communicate to it the peculiar spirit and virtues of Pyrmont water, and other mineral waters of a similar nature* was put in hand. The appearance of the pamphlet caused an immediate stir both in this country and overseas, and a French translation appeared soon afterwards. Priestley was exhilarated. Looking back on this a few years later, he regarded it as his happiest idea, though, he said, it had the least scientific merit of all his discoveries.

Chapter 6

Different Kinds of Air

As PRIESTLEY's output had been continuous for several years, it
seemed scarcely possible that he should still have more useful
and more important materials in reserve. Yet the new series of
papers he wrote for the Royal Society in the autumn of 1771,
and which were read in the following March, contained so
many novel discoveries that they immediately established his
reputation as one of the outstanding experimentalists of the day.
In the first published account (at the end of 1772) [1] he made
known the results of five years' work on one of the great
scientific problems of that age—the part played by the atmosphere in a variety of natural processes, including the life of
plants and animals, and the nature of other 'airs'.

The impact of these studies, though considerable in Great
Britain, was even more notable in some European countries,
and it was frequently said that the close attention paid to the
work of British men of science throughout the next two decades
was due largely to the interest, even excitement, aroused by
Priestley's papers on different kinds of air.

How was it that, in this difficult and obscure field, he was
able to make advances that had eluded so many men of science?
He himself put it down to his habit of searching into dark and
mysterious corners, and of following a scent wherever it might
lead, without any preconceived ideas. Almost alone among
scientists then living, he was honest enough to credit part at
least of his success to enthusiasm and a sense of adventure. If
he was looking at a piece of mint standing in an upturned jar
over a bowl of water, or at a mouse in an inverted beer-glass,

[1] H. Guerlac, *J. Hist. Med.*, 1957, *12*, 1–12. Guerlac's date (October 1772) is a
little too early (internal evidence). See also D. McKie, 'Joseph Priestley and the
Copley Medal', *Ambix*, 1961, *9* (1), 1–22.

great issues were at stake. He was watching carefully for any hint that might lead to means for enhancing the welfare and happiness of mankind. And behind it all he was convinced that the rapid progress of knowledge would 'be the means, under God, of extirpating all error and prejudice, and of putting an end to all undue and usurped authority in the business of religion, as well as of science'.

Early Discoveries about Air

Before we can assess this work, it is necessary to know what had already been discovered, and what these discoveries meant to scientists at the time. Oliver Goldsmith, in a posthumous book on science, had written an account of 'air' at about the time Priestley was making his experiments. It gave a picture of current ideas and showed how puzzling the whole subject had become. The most important point that emerges is that air was still universally thought of as a simple elementary substance. Its physical properties had been studied and measured. Many of its effects on other substances had been recorded, but little thought had been given to the possibility of studying it as a chemical material.

It was shown by Bacon that air had the property of elasticity, that is, it could be expanded and compressed. Galileo showed that air had weight. One of his pupils, Torricelli, by a single experiment, showed how to measure the pressure of the atmosphere. Soon afterwards von Guericke invented the air-pump, which, in the hands of Boyle, became a valuable scientific instrument. Boyle made numerous studies of the air and its effects. Though much of this work was physical in outlook, both Boyle and Hooke examined some of the chemical effects of air, and they contributed a little to the study of the air itself as a chemical substance.

One of the most significant questions Boyle asked himself about air was whether a fluid of such obvious and great utility could not be produced artificially. In a series of new experiments, he obtained an 'elastic fluid' in several ways from ripe fruit, from fermenting and effervescing liquors, and from putrefying animal and vegetable substances. He then found that these 'productions of art' did not have the desired properties, for they extinguished a flame and killed small animals, such as mice. He therefore distinguished such elastic fluids by the name of 'factitious' or 'artificial' air. He was the first, according to Priestley, to realize that there might be other elastic fluids than common air.

By the views it learns or adopts about Nature, each generation is limited as to the progress it can make in natural knowledge. Boyle had taken the subject as far as he could, and for many years it seemed pointless to try to add anything to this very thorough work. Newton, in his *Opticks*, noted that heat and fermentation gave rise to permanently elastic air from many bodies and that such air could return into even dense substances. That 'airs' could be extracted from animal substances was also of interest to some Dutch physicists and chemists. Thus Musschenbroeck, working at Leyden as a medical student under Boerhaave, prepared a thesis on the subject in 1715. Boerhaave himself made a special study of fermentation not long afterwards, though his own account of it was not published until 1732. He gave close attention to the 'wild spirit' or 'gas'—as his compatriot van Helmont had called it in the previous century—that was released during fermentation. Yet, as a physician, he failed to understand how this air could bring about death without causing any disease, or without causing any apparent alteration in the brain, nerves, juices or solids in the body. Such ideas as he could form brought him to make a similar suggestion to Boyle's, the significance of which was noticed by Macbride, who seems to have been the first to draw attention to it: 'whether there be not in Nature, something like common elastic air, without being air'.

Meanwhile Stephen Hales had followed up the work of Boyle in the light of Newton's comment, and had obtained air by 'fire and fermentation' from a large number of vegetable, animal, and mineral substances. He also made very numerous measurements of the volume of air obtained in relation to the weight of substance taken, thereby showing how great was the quantity of air that could be separated in these ways. Hales at this time included effervescence under fermentation, and so a wide range of chemical reactions was covered. Later on he

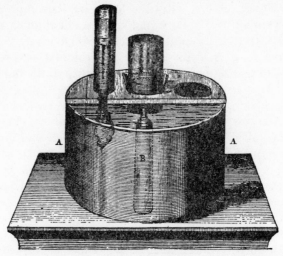

Fig. 5 Brownrigg's pneumatic apparatus.

followed Boerhaave in distinguishing the two processes. Many similar measurements were made by Musschenbroeck in Holland. Although Hales had various new elastic fluids in his apparatus from time to time, he nowhere gave any indication that he thought of them as anything other than common air. He also examined mineral waters, then of much use in medicine, and noticed that some of them, especially those from Pyrmont, gave large quantities of air, to which he thought they owed their briskness.

Progress on more suggestive lines was made by William Brownrigg, who obtained a medical degree at Leyden. Though he turned to such questions in about 1740 and wrote papers for the Royal Society in 1741, none of this work was published until 1765. He then described his extraction of 'the mineral elastic spirit, or air' from Spa water. This was done in a long thin bottle with a bladder attached to its neck (Fig. 5). When 'air' was released, the bladder became distended. The air was then transferred from the bladder to a large open-mouthed bottle supported by a rack attached to the side of a trough filled with water. In this bottle the properties of the air could be examined. This simple, though crucially important apparatus, which is generally credited to Priestley rather than Brownrigg, became known later as the 'pneumatic trough' (or the 'hydro-pneumatic tub', as the French more accurately called it).

In the course of his work Brownrigg noted that the noxious 'damps' in mines, such as choke-damp, were similar to what was called the 'spirit' of certain mineral waters, and he found that choke-damp was not merely a vapour or exhalation but a permanently elastic fluid. He also concluded that the waters of Pyrmont, Spa, and some other springs owed their acidulous taste to this volatile principle, to which also their medicinal virtues could be traced.

Several years later, when on the Continent, Brownrigg made further experiments which showed that Boyle's factitious air was the same as the suffocating air in certain Italian caves—like the Grotta de' Cani near Naples—and the choke-damp of the English mines. His tests for this were the immediate extinction of a flame and the sudden death of small animals, such as mice.

Brownrigg must be credited with having advanced beyond the views of Hales in showing that there were chemically different kinds of elastic fluids. In his early papers he asked that chemists would study these—not merely their effects—as it seemed a promising field of inquiry. To this end it would be necessary 'to consider those substances from which they are produced; by exact experiments to detect their properties when native and simple; to inquire what changes may result from their coalitions and combinations amongst one another . . .'. This was a truly chemical point of view. The particles of dense bodies were not always reduced to air, but to different kinds of elastic fluids which frequently retain the properties of the dense bodies from which they are generated.

This, it seems, was the challenge Priestley accepted: to determine, by their chemical behaviour, what different kinds of elastic fluids there are. Often it has been taken for granted that Priestley set out to study the different kinds of *air*, but this is scarcely accurate. His work, which continued for many years, was a prolonged study of different *kinds* of elastic fluids, or 'species' of air *sui generis*. His plan was nothing less than a voyage of discovery and observation to map out a new *terra incognita*. If we forget this, we are liable to gain the impression that Priestley, darting as he often did from one topic to another, did not himself know what he was trying to do; with a man of his steadfastness of purpose, such a conclusion would be entirely out of character.

Joseph Black in Scotland had made by far the most important chemical advance in the study of the way 'air' could form part of the composition of dense bodies. In a series of experiments lasting over some years, he found that a particular factitious air (which he called 'fixed air') could be obtained from chalk, magnesia, soda, and potash by means of acids, and that this fixed air entered into their composition. It could be separated from them and united with their alkalis in the same way as an acid. This explained many reactions in which effervescence took place, and also the difference between caustic and mild alkalis, the fixed air mollifying the 'fiery' properties of the former. Thus quicklime absorbs fixed air and becomes chalk.

Black introduced a simple chemical test for fixed air—in its presence lime-water goes turbid—and this made it possible for him to show that fixed air was the same as choke-damp, the same as the 'wild gas' produced during fermentation, and the same as the volatile ingredient of acidulous spring waters; and that it was produced in the combustion of charcoal and in animal respiration.

Whereas choke-damp settles in caves and lower parts of mines and in cellars, fire-damp collects in the domes or upper parts of enclosed spaces. Such inflammable air Brownrigg led off from a nearby mine into his laboratory at Whitehaven and used to heat his furnaces. In the 1730s Sir James Lowther, who owned the mines there, had sent some bladders filled with the air to the Royal Society, and it had been burnt at one of the meetings. Brownrigg also obtained inflammable air from peas.

Cavendish studied the inflammable factitious air obtained by pouring some acids on to some metals. The same air was obtained whether diluted oil of vitriol (sulphuric acid) or spirit of sea-salt (hydrochloric acid) was used, and if the metal was zinc, iron, or tin. This air (later called hydrogen) was what Cavendish and most chemists of the period meant by inflammable air, but the term gave rise to confusion. For it was not Brownrigg's inflammable air (fire-damp, methane) nor the inflammable airs that Priestley made not many years afterwards (carbon monoxide and coal-gas). Cavendish introduced another means of distinguishing between airs—by measuring their specific gravities. Thus he found that inflammable air (from metals) was only a tenth as heavy, and fixed air half as heavy again, as common air.

Priestley's Early Studies

From this introduction it might easily be assumed that only a small step remained to be taken before the whole chemistry of the gases would become apparent. But Priestley as a historian maintained that the gulf between knowledge and ignorance remains complete until the final step has been taken—and this can scarcely be denied. If we look at the latest encyclopedia available in 1765, the *General Dictionary of Arts and Sciences*, we shall find articles under both 'gas' and 'air', and a hasty look might give the impression that knowledge of these topics was considerable. But 'gas' was defined as a term made use of by van Helmont and chemists generally to signify 'spirit incapable of coagulation, such as proceeds from fermented wine'. The article on 'air' made an even more revealing admission: 'To speak the truth, our knowledge of the substance and intimate nature of the air amounts to a very small matter; what authors have hitherto said about it being but mere conjecture. There is no way of examining air pure and defecated from the several things which are intermixed with it: consequently there is no saying what is its particular nature.'

Priestley must have spent some part of his leisure in the autumn of 1767, and the following winter, in reading all he could about earlier work on air, repeating much of it and making experiments of his own. Fixed air he obtained at first from the brewery, but, after he had left the neighbourhood, he adopted Black's method of adding diluted oil of vitriol to chalk; he made inflammable air by Cavendish's method, and his first experiments were made with these two airs. Right from the start, he found the work full of interest and surprises. Writing to Price on 16 January 1768 he said,[1] in a passage that the editor of his correspondence omitted:

[1] Bodleian MS. Eng. Misc. c. 132, f. 5b.

My experiments on *Air* I find will run out to a great length, several new circumstances have occurred, which I cannot yet ascertain, and some of the operations require several weeks before they are completed. The late frost broke me 4 or 5 Jars, in which I had several processes, which had been going on above a month. I shall not renew them till I return from London.

He was shortly leaving for his annual visit to the metropolis. Inflammable air, he had found, when freshly made from steel filings and diluted oil of vitriol, kills animals as suddenly as any mephitic air (Plate 8). He had not yet learnt how to obtain airs perfectly free from common air, and his results did not always seem to tally with one another, but with practice he was quickly becoming expert in this new and tricky field of manipulation. He had already noticed the fact of diffusion:

. . . a narrow necked phial filled with inflammable air, and suspended, with its mouth downwards, or with mephitic air, and placed with its mouth upwards, will in a short time be found to contain nothing but common air . . .

He had also carried out experiments in which he noted the colours of electric sparks formed in the airs.

With all his other occupations, it is not surprising that his work on this subject took a long time; indeed it was not until the early autumn of 1771 that he wrote up his first collection of results, and sent them to Franklin for the Royal Society. These experiments were grouped together under subjects, and it is now no longer possible to follow strictly the order in which they were carried out.

Before the results were published, Priestley added some new findings up to November 1772, given in a further paper to the Society in that month. Fourcroy, who wrote about this work twenty years later, and was able to assess its influence as well as any other chemical historian of the period, said that it opened out a wholly new vista of fresh fields of scientific inquiry on a scale that had never been known before. Priestley's new observations, indeed, amounted to more than the whole of what had been previously known or done on the subject. For ease of reference the names given to the gases, and their more modern equivalents, are listed on pp. 81–2.

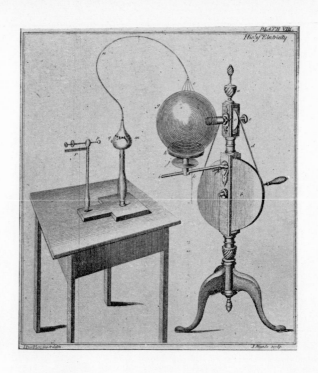

Plate 7 Priestley's electrical machine, designed in 1768, from his own drawing. One of these machines is in the possession of the Royal Society.

Plate 8 Priestley's early apparatus for pneumatic experiments. His jars were those used for electrical work; the mouse is shown in an inverted beer-glass; the jar in the foreground stands in a tea-dish; the trough was of the kind used for washing linen.

Fixed Air

Some of Priestley's work on fixed air, which led to the introduction of 'aerated' (carbonated) waters, has already been described (p. 57). He went on to say that beer, wine, and cider, if they had become flat, could be improved by impregnation with fixed air, though the taste of the fixed air could then be hardly detected. Ice would not absorb fixed air, and if Pyrmont water was frozen it looked more like snow than ice, owing to the release of the fixed air. Pyrmont water, beer, and ale soon boil in an exhausted receiver, as the fixed air comes off so quickly. The pressure of the atmosphere therefore assists in keeping the fixed air confined in the water, and so the amount of fixed air taken up by water could be increased by the use of a compressing engine. On this principle a whole new industry —the manufacture of artificial mineral waters—was based (Fig. 6).

He also took fixed air from the vat and tried its effect on a variety of living things, not merely mice, but also insects, frogs, snails, and growing plants, and found that there was a great variety in the time taken to kill them. The colours of plants were also affected in different ways by fixed air. A red rose turned purple, another became colourless, and various other plants were unaffected.

From chalk and acid he obtained very pure fixed air—less than a fiftieth part was insoluble in water; he tested this small residuum and found that a mouse would live in it, though a candle would not burn. He thought he had discovered a case of genuine common air being generated from a solid, but this idea had to be abandoned later. It did, however, prompt him to try to convert fixed air into common air.

Priestley knew from Lemery that a moistened mixture of iron filings and sulphur reacted in the atmosphere, and by carrying out such an experiment in a tube above quicksilver he had found that the volume of air had been reduced by a fifth. Repeating this in fixed air he found a similar result, and so far as he could judge, the process appeared to be the same. On examining the 'air' afterwards he found that as much as a sixth of it had become insoluble in water. Was this common air? No, for a mouse died 'pretty soon'.

As he had not obtained an answer to his immediate question, he left the subject for others to do what they could with it. It was not his purpose to be side-tracked by any incidental observations however intriguing. He was setting a trail. Others would pick it up, and in this way natural knowledge would grow the faster.

Deprived of the brewery's supply of fixed air, he thought the

Fig. 6 Early apparatus for impregnating water under pressure. Vanes inside the barrel facilitated the mixing of water and gas. A model made by Adam Walker for his popular science lectures.

easiest way to prepare it would be to heat chalk in a gun-barrel and pass the 'air' through a clay pipe into a receiver (Plate 9). He did this, and air was produced plentifully. He was surprised to find, however, that only about half of it was fixed air; the rest was highly inflammable. Now iron and acid produce inflammable air. Had it, then, been produced from the metal of the gun-barrel and the acid (fixed air) in the chalk? He was, of course, on the right track, but he was already too good an experimentalist to be caught out as easily as this! For this inflammable air (now known as carbon monoxide) burned with a blue flame and not at all like Cavendish's inflammable air. This led to a different and somewhat unprofitable train of thought, and he left it at that.

Diminution of Air

Priestley went on to examine common air in which a candle, or sulphur, had burned out. Though the iron-and-sulphur mixture reduced the air by about a fifth, burning objects were extinguished after only one-fifteenth to one-sixteenth of the air had been 'consumed'. He was not happy about this word, which he thought implied too much, and was unscientific. The diminution of the air in this instance was only about one-third of the former, or of the amount by which it is diminished when animal and vegetable substances are allowed to putrefy in it or when metals are calcined. If lime-water is exposed while a candle is burning, it goes turbid. The same result occurred with all the burning objects he tried, except with sulphur. He came to the conclusion that whenever a process caused the air to be diminished in volume, there was a precipitation of the 'fixed part of the air'. This was not the same as fixed air, for it occurred with sulphur and with metals, and in neither of these cases was fixed air produced. With a candle this could be seen to happen when lime-water was present. With sulphur it could not be seen to happen, but if the lime-water was evaporated, a substance rather similar to chalk remained behind.

Though a candle that had burned to extinction in a quantity of air could not be re-lit in the same air, sulphur could be re-lit more than once, though not indefinitely. Previous workers, such as Hales, imagined that processes like these could be continued until all the air had been 'consumed'. Priestley's work had shown that this was not so; a limit was reached when about a fifth of the air had gone, that is, when the whole of the fixable part of the air had been 'precipitated'.

At this time Priestley regarded the air as compounded [1] of two parts—the air remaining after diminution being one part (later called nitrogen), and the portion that had been precipitated being the other (afterwards isolated by Priestley and by Scheele, and called oxygen by Lavoisier). He measured the

[1] The terms 'mixture' and 'compound' were as yet almost synonymous; 'decomposition' signified separation of the ingredients.

density of the remaining air and found it *lighter* than common air; therefore, he concluded, the fixed part of the air is the heavier. These diminution experiments he regarded as proof of the 'decomposition' of the air. He was feeling his way, and the clearest statement that can be found on the matter is this:

After making several trials . . . I concluded that air, thus diminished in bulk, is rather lighter than common air, which favours the supposition of the fixed, or heavier part of the common air, having been precipitated.

It would be of interest to know when he first came to this conclusion. A search of letters and the writings of Priestley's acquaintances might be expected to reveal something, for they were always the first to be informed of his discoveries. However, only one suggestive statement has been found. This is a footnote which John Warltire, an itinerant lecturer on science and one of Priestley's friends, added to the sixth edition of his lecture notes, dated 1769. One of these lectures dealt with the fact that the air 'is necessary to the Growth of Vegetables, and to Animal Life'. The next note shows that he used the same language as Priestley when speaking of these things: 'May be vitiated either by the Introduction of foreign Matter, or by Decomposition.' The footnote reads: 'The Atmosphere is composed of two distinct Sorts of fluid Matter, one capable of being so attracted by certain Bodies as to become fixed; the other always retains its elastic Quality.' [1]

William Lewis, in 1763–5, had pointed out that the only reason chemists had been able to give for the increase in weight of metals when calcined was the absorption (or fixation) of air. Priestley had shown that only part of the air was fixable, and Warltire appears to have known that the other part in such processes always retained its elastic quality. These statements of Priestley and Warltire are necessarily vague, for no one yet had any idea as to what the fixable part of the air was; it was not yet properly distinguished from Black's fixed air.

---

[1] Many historians credit the discovery of the two main constituents of the atmosphere to Scheele. Some later scientists, such as Dalton, who better understood the language of the period than we can today, did not hesitate to credit the discovery to Priestley.

Restoration of Noxious Air

Priestley's interest in what makes air noxious and what restores it to a wholesome state had been of long standing, for he speaks of having had certain thoughts for 'a long time' and refers to experiments tried out 'many years ago'. For example, it had been maintained that air in which a candle had burned out could be restored by cold and compression. Priestley repeated these experiments and found that the air was not improved. It was restored when he compressed it with a bladder, but he had cause to suspect bladders and repeated it in a glass vessel. There was no doubt that such treatment did not change it at all. It had also been stated that heat alone made air unfit for candles to burn in. Priestley knew this to be untrue, for 'many years ago' he had filled an exhausted receiver with air that had passed through a red-hot glass tube, and had found that a candle would burn in it perfectly well.

Nevertheless he did hit on a genuine means of restoring air in which a candle had burned out. It opened up a whole new view of how Nature operates. Everyone knew that animals could not be kept in confined spaces unless the air were changed at intervals. It was taken for granted that the same was true for plants.

I own I had that expectation, when I first put a sprig of mint into a glass-jar, standing inverted in a vessel of water: but when it had continued growing there for some months, I found that the air would neither extinguish a candle, nor was it at all inconvenient to a mouse, which I put into it.

He therefore wondered what would happen if he put the mint into air in which a candle had burned out. It was now the summer of 1771. The sprig of mint was put in on 17 August, and on 27 August a candle burned in it again perfectly well. He repeated the experiment about ten times before the summer ended. Similar experiments were repeated in the following summer, and he found the same effect with groundsel, and the quickest result with spinach.

Inflammable Air

Priestley found he could obtain inflammable air, not only by adding dilute acids to metals, but also by heating chalk, coal, and a variety of animal and vegetable materials in a gun-barrel. He thus had several different inflammable airs, and it is not a matter for surprise that the topic should have proved too difficult for him to make many important observations. He found that plants whose leaves were enclosed in Cavendish's inflammable air continued to grow, and that the air was still inflammable after six months. However, it was just as noxious to animals as was fixed air. Here was another clear difference between plants and animals. He wondered if the two airs would 'mix' (we would say react) to give common air, and exploded a mixture of them over mercury, but it taught him no more. He sparked some inflammable air mixed with the fumes of strong spirit of nitre. This 'goes off at one explosion', but again leads no nearer to anything resembling common air.

Respired Air and Putrid Air

He turned to 'air infected with animal respiration, or putrefaction'. Here he reasoned more and experimented less, concluding that animals died in such air, not from the lack of anything, but from its being impregnated with something that stimulated their lungs, for they always died in convulsions in this as in any other kind of noxious air. Later work was to show how wrong this view was. He did, however, notice that a mouse put into air that became slowly more vitiated lasted longer than one put straight into badly vitiated air. Thus, he said, if the experiment of the Black Hole of Calcutta was repeated, a man entering at first would stand a better chance of surviving than a man going in much later. This paradox took many years to explain.

While working at the topic, Priestley wondered if air in this condition could not be restored by chemical means. In the previous century Mayow, in a brilliantly suggestive study, had called the unknown supporter of life in the atmosphere by the name of nitro-aerial spirit. Priestley also knew that, in the absence of air, substances would continue to burn only if mixed with nitre or saltpetre. He wondered if the acid of nitre might not be one of Nature's restoratives. He therefore took some saltpetre, which was a salt of that acid, and extracted an air from it by heat. His idea was strengthened by finding that candles would burn in it. All unwittingly he had come very close to his goal. But although he had prepared oxygen he had not discovered it. All he had done was to confirm a line of reasoning. He kept some of this air by him for more than a year, as it was still necessary for him to be economical. But he did not yet know how to reconcile this new observation with his belief that 'in all vitiating processes, the compound mass of air is disposed to part with some constituent part belonging to it'. This experiment was made around October 1771, and he had to wait nearly four years for the solution to his problem.

Priestley's observations on putrefaction led to some interesting and unfamiliar findings. Beef or mutton kept over mercury for a few days at above body temperature produced air that was about one-seventh soluble (fixed air), the rest being inflammable. Vegetables treated similarly did not yield inflammable air, but fixed air. Plants and some insects lived very well in putrid air, and this made him wonder if plants reversed the effects of breathing. Accordingly he devised experiments with sprigs of mint, which have already been described.

Such experiments he repeated in the summer of 1772. On 20 June he prepared the air by allowing mice to die in it. A week later a sprig of mint that had been put into it looked remarkably healthy, and the air had been restored enough for a candle to burn and a mouse to breathe in it. On that occasion the experiments were seen by witnesses—no other than Franklin and Sir John Pringle, President of the Royal Society, who had visited him before going on to see Brownrigg in Cumberland. Perhaps they were already wondering if his work merited the Copley Medal, which was awarded annually by the Society. In a subsequent letter Franklin reasoned that the 'air is mended by taking something from it, and not by adding to it'. More than a dozen years passed before Priestley discovered that both occurred. Franklin went on: 'I hope this will give some check to the rage of destroying trees that grow near houses.'

Measuring the Goodness of Air

|Another promising line of investigation seemed to be an experiment of Hales in which he noticed an air that formed a red turbid mixture with common air, absorbing part of it in the process. Hales had obtained it by adding spirit of nitre to 'Walton pyrites'. Priestley knew nothing about this mineral and so, when in London at the time his papers were being read, he asked Cavendish's advice. Cavendish, who may have remembered some experiments carried out by Boyle and Hooke, suggested that metals might give the same result. On his return to Leeds, Priestley began with brass and spirit of nitre on 4 June and obtained the gas he wanted at his first attempt. Knowing no name for it, he began to call it 'nitrous air'. The same air was given with iron, copper, brass, tin, silver, mercury, bismuth, and nickel, and so Cavendish was right. When Priestley mixed this colourless air with common air, heat was generated and there was a considerable diminution in volume, together with a turbid red or deep orange colour which spread throughout the vessel. The diminution, he found, corresponded to a fifth of the common air and as much of the nitrous air as was necessary to produce the effect—about a third of the volume of air taken. He repeated it over mercury and found only a small change of volume. Thus in the former experiment the water had dissolved the red product. He concluded that he had found a direct means of measuring the 'fitness of the air for respiration', which must be proportional to the diminution. By means of somewhat elongated tubes, volume changes could be measured accurately, and there would no longer be occasion to keep a large stock of mice handy at all times.

On 21 July he wrote about this to Price:

One third of this kind of air mixed with two thirds of common air makes it hot, red, and turbid for some time, and is so far from making any addition to the bulk of it, that it considerably diminishes it. By this means I have a very large scale of mensuration. It has no sensible effect on air unfit for respiration, on whatever account it be so.

This was a most important advance, as accurate measurements of chemical changes in the atmosphere became possible for the first time. It ushered in a period when the air in many different localities was examined by means of equipment shortly to be known as 'eudiometers', literally 'purity measurers' (Plate 10). This new means of analysis was of considerable general interest, not merely to science, but also to medicine and public health. And all this was done some years before oxygen was known.

Priestley went on to examine the properties of nitrous air. He mixed it with inflammable air, and found that it then burned with a green flame. He thought at first this might be due to copper from the preparation, but found the same colour whatever the metal used. Having a taste for making interesting demonstrations for his friends, he found that by mixing oil of vitriol with a smaller quantity of spirit of nitre, and adding the metal, he could produce the green-burning mixture in one operation.

He then tried whether the paste of iron filings and sulphur would have any effect on nitrous air, and discovered that the latter was diminished until only about a quarter remained. The action became visible after five to six hours and then was completed in another hour. So far as he could tell, the remaining air (nitrogen) was just the same as if he had started with common air. He felt that he was still on the track of something that resembled common air; but plants soon died in nitrous air, even if mixed with common air. He was also surprised to find that nineteen-twentieths of his nitrous air was dissolved by boiled water. He then impregnated water with it and found that it acquired a remarkably acid taste. He concluded, in phraseology similar to that used by Brownrigg, that part of the spirit of nitre remained in the composition of nitrous air. Like fixed air, it checked putrefaction, and he thought their powers in this connection might be in proportion to their acidities.

Fumes of Burning Charcoal

Cavendish had found that air was diminished in volume when it was passed through a heated tube packed with charcoal dust. Priestley repeated the experiment with almost the same result. He then suspended a lump of charcoal in a glass vessel over water and heated it with a burning lens, when the air was reduced in volume by a fifth. Lime-water showed that fixed air was produced. He thought at first that the fixed air came from the charcoal, then that it was deposited from the air. But he decided that the experiment was inconclusive and recommended it for further investigation. He tried it again over mercury, and this time there was no diminution until lime-water was added, when a reduction of a fifth occurred as before. He weighed the charcoal, but could not tell that it had lost any weight. Once more his method had been scientific, but it was only several years later that the true explanation of the observations was found.

At this point, though his facts were inconclusive, Priestley felt able to say that Hales was definitely mistaken in thinking that common air was absorbed in the various processes when diminution occurred. For Hales had supposed that the part of the air left was of the same nature as the part absorbed, and that the operation of the same cause would bring about a further diminution. But his own experiments had shown that air could be diminished only by a definite amount, and that in the process it acquired new properties.

Calcination of Metals, and Lead Paints

Calcination, he thought, should provide the *experimentum crucis* on this point. He suspended pieces of lead and tin in air over mercury and heated them with a burning lens. In one such experiment a diminution as large as a quarter was observed, but nearly always it was a fifth. The remaining air was not able to support any further calcination. It was 'noxious in the highest degree', it did not have any effect on nitrous air, and it could not be further diminished by the mixture of iron filings and sulphur.

This may well have been the first unequivocal preparation of the gas later known as nitrogen. Daniel Rutherford, in a medical thesis at Edinburgh, published in September 1772, had described experiments in which mice were allowed to breathe in a confined volume of air, and the fixed air was afterwards removed with caustic potash. The residue, which was not fixed air, was noxious to animals and extinguished flame, but gave no precipitate with lime-water. But the diminutions reported by Rutherford were smaller than Priestley's, and Rutherford lacked a method of showing if the noxious air was capable of any further diminution.

Priestley went on to examine the cause of the dangerous properties of fresh paint made with white-lead. He daubed pieces of paper with the paint and hung them in a receiver. After twenty-four hours the air was diminished by at least a fifth and had become noxious. It underwent no further diminution with nitrous air or with iron filings and sulphur. This had obvious applications in everyday life.

Marine Acid Air

Another discovery followed directly from an experiment made by Cavendish, who had been surprised that he could get no inflammable air from copper and spirit of salt. On heating he got instead a more remarkable kind of air, for it immediately lost its elasticity on coming into contact with water. Priestley repeated this, but collected the air over mercury. On admitting a little water, the air was reduced to a quarter of its volume; the remainder he found to be inflammable air. He repeated the experiment with lead, and obtained a similar result. By admitting only a small quantity of water at a time, he found that the latter could be saturated with the new air, and he obtained the strongest spirit of salt he had ever seen. He then found that he could obtain this air as easily as before by heating the acid by itself, so that this 'marine acid air' (hydrogen chloride) was nothing but the vapour or fumes of spirit of salt. He noted that it extinguished a flame, and was much heavier than common air. He also introduced a variety of substances into it. Iron filings reacted fast, and half the acid air disappeared; the remaining half was inflammable air, not absorbed by water. Chalk gave up its fixed air. Although spirit of salt was the weakest of the common mineral acids, the acid air displaced the stronger acids of alum and nitre.

Back to Saltpetre

On 6 November 1772 Priestley re-examined some of the air
he had extracted from saltpetre more than a year previously.
His purpose was to see what effect the nitrous-air test would
have on it. It reacted 'as much as the best common air ever
does', and a candle burned in it well. These facts, he said,
'appear to me very extraordinary and important, and, in able
hands, may lead to considerable discoveries'. In the hands of
Scheele, the Swedish apothecary's assistant, similar experiments
led to the independent discovery of oxygen, although Priestley
was not aware of this at the time he wrote. Later, looking back
on this work, Priestley could only think that he had not seen
what actually occurred in these tests, being so utterly convinced
at this time that nothing could be purer than common air.

*

This is an outline of the main facts and observations Priestley
had made by the end of 1772 and for which he was awarded
the Copley Medal in the following year. The experiments were
epoch-making, in that they provided a mass of new material
for others to work upon, and added a new dimension to chemical
thought. Priestley's aim, indeed, was being realized; he had
set the ball rolling; his enthusiasm was to prove infectious, and
he was to see a rapid extension of natural knowledge resulting
to a considerable extent from his own efforts. Was he right to
move on hastily to new fields? Would it not have been better if
he had concentrated on a few crucial experiments and helped
to advance science in a more systematic manner? Had he done
so, he would have discovered less, and would have been less
generally useful to his generation. He excelled in observation
and knew that he was weaker in interpreting his results. As on
previous occasions, he wanted to interest people in science and
to make others join in—a thing of much more consequence to
the public than even his own reputation as a scientist.

The Copley Medal was presented to Priestley at the anniversary meeting of the Royal Society on 30 November 1773.
On this occasion Sir John Pringle created a precedent by giving
an address to point out the importance of this work in its

historical setting. In his final summing up of Priestley's major contributions to science, Pringle showed that wide views of Nature's operations were at last emerging.

From these discoveries we are assured, that no vegetable grows in vain, but that from the oak of the forest to the grass of the field, every individual plant is serviceable to mankind; if not always distinguished by some private virtue, yet making a part of the whole which cleanses and purifies our atmosphere. In this the fragrant rose and deadly nightshade co-operate; nor is the herbage, nor the woods that flourish in the most remote and unpeopled regions unprofitable to us, nor we to them; considering how constantly the winds convey to them our vitiated air, for our relief, and for their nourishment. And if ever these salutary gales rise to storms and hurricanes, let us still trace and revere the ways of a beneficent Being; who not fortuitously but with design, not in wrath but in mercy, thus shakes the waters and the air together, to bury in the deep those putrid and pestilential *effluvia*, which the vegetables upon the face of the earth had been insufficient to consume.

Priestley's Terminology

SUBSTANCE	MODERN EQUIVALENT
Acid air	Earliest name for hydrogen chloride
Alkaline air	Ammonia
Choke-damp	Carbon dioxide. *See* Fixed air
Combined fixed air	Carbon monoxide (but not recognized as a distinct substance for many years to come)
Common air	The air composing the earth's atmosphere
Dephlogisticated air	Oxygen
Dephlogisticated nitrous air	Nitrous oxide
Fire-damp	Methane. *See* Inflammable air
Fixable air	Usually confused with, and later restricted to, Black's fixed air
Fixed air	Carbon dioxide
Fluor acid air	Silicon tetrafluoride
Inflammable air	Usually hydrogen (light inflammable air) or carbon monoxide (heavy inflammable air). Also confused with methane, coal-gas, etc.
Marine acid air	Hydrogen chloride

Mephitic air	Generally, any unwholesome air unfit for breathing; specifically, fixed air
Modified nitrous air	Nitrous oxide
Muriatic acid air	*See* Marine acid air
Nitre	Potassium nitrate
Nitrous acid	Nitric acid
Nitrous air	Nitric oxide
Noxious air	Common air lacking in oxygen. *See* Vitiated air
Oil of vitriol	Strong sulphuric acid
Phlogisticated air	Nitrogen
Phlogisticated nitrous air	Nitrous oxide (more correct name; *see* Dephlogisticated nitrous air)
Pure air	Oxygen
Putrid air	Common air in which animal or vegetable material had been allowed to putrefy
Red nitrous vapour	Nitrogen dioxide (with or without nitric oxide or oxygen)
Sal ammoniac	Ammonium chloride
Spirit of salt	Hydrochloric acid
Sulphurated inflammable air	Hydrogen sulphide
Vitiated air	Air not fit for respiration—as a result of respiration, combustion, or other 'phlogistic' process
Vitriolic acid air	Sulphur dioxide
Vitriolic fumes	Sulphur trioxide
Volatile spirit of sal ammoniac	Ammonia solution
Volatile vitriolic acid	Sulphur dioxide solution (sulphurous acid)

Phlogiston

It is observed fact that fuels and certain metals are active substances that on burning or calcination give out light and heat and leave an inactive ash or calx. In the jargon of the nuclear age, an active 'fuel' releases energy in the pile and leaves an inactive (or less active) 'ash'. In the eighteenth century, until the time of Lavoisier, it was widely believed that 'phlogiston' was the common principle in all fuels and calcinable metals, and that it was released during combustion and calcination.

In Priestley's time phlogiston had a double part to play. On the one hand, it was thought of as akin to heat, light, and electricity. On the other hand, until the role of oxygen was more correctly explained by Lavoisier and his colleagues, it was also regarded as a substance. In reality, a supposed loss of phlogiston was often a gain of oxygen; and a gain of phlogiston was a loss of oxygen or a gain of hydrogen. Thus phlogistication was frequently equivalent to reduction, and dephlogistication to oxidation.

The idea of phlogiston eventually became too overloaded and overworked to be a useful hypothesis any longer. Priestley supplied much of the evidence for a simpler and more rational interpretation, but he did not admit the fact and exerted himself to the last in defence of the term. Lavoisier distinguished the two main functions of phlogiston, but he was forced to retain its energy characteristics in the concept of *calorique*.

Chapter 7

Shelburne House and Bowood

By the time Priestley's papers on different kinds of air were being read to the Royal Society and his history of light was published, he was receiving overtures from the Earl of Shelburne, who wished to take him into his service.

William Petty, the second earl of Shelburne (Plate 6), was descended on his father's side from the earls of Kerry, and through the female line he inherited the name and large fortune of Sir William Petty, the renowned financier and scientist of the seventeenth century. For a short time Petty became aide-de-camp to George III on his accession in 1760, and in the following year he succeeded to the Irish earldom of Shelburne and the English barony of Wycombe. He was an able politician and in 1766 became a member of the Earl of Chatham's cabinet. He opposed the King's policy over the American colonies, and was dismissed from the post of Secretary of State in 1768. Now out of office, he strenuously opposed Lord North's measures, and especially his colonial policy. North's government lingered on until 1782, and in that year Shelburne himself took office as Prime Minister. During North's administration it seemed to Priestley and his friends that the King was exerting far too much influence over Parliament, so jeopardizing the relatively young 'cabinet' system and rendering the House of Commons almost ineffective.

Shelburne had a genuine interest in Priestley's writings and scientific work, and admired his abilities. When Price hinted to him that Priestley needed a patron, he quickly decided what to do. Shelburne's approach was made with tact and appeared more as an offer of employment than as patronage, no doubt to avoid giving the slightest offence to a man of proudly independent spirit. Priestley was asked to look after Shelburne's

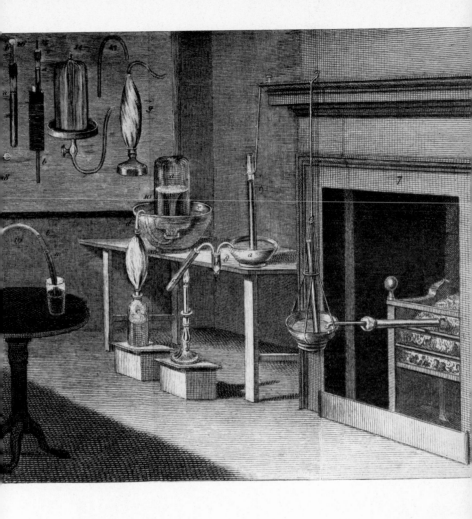

Plate 9 Priestley's electrical and chemical apparatus in 1774. From right to left: a gun-barrel luted to a clay pipe for preparing inflammable air from chalk; preparation of alkaline air from quicklime and sal ammoniac; early apparatus for impregnating water with fixed air.

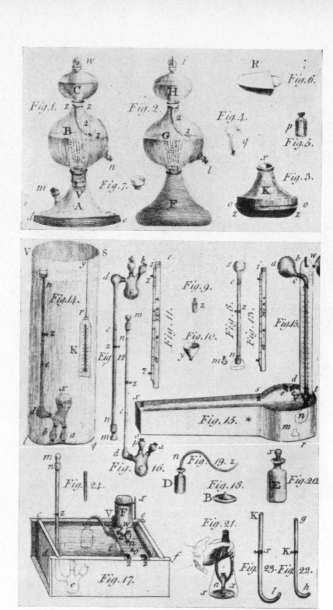

Plate 10 Magellan's adaptation (1777) of (*above*) Nooth's apparatus for making impregnated water; (*below*) Landriani's eudiometers for measuring the 'purity' of air with nitric oxide.

library, superintend the education of his two young sons (whose mother had died in 1771), and collect materials on subjects under discussion in Parliament (*see* Plate 11). To many men this would have seemed a full-time appointment, if not a heavy task. For Shelburne maintained princely homes in town and country, kept himself better informed than any minister of state, and, like Priestley, regarded education as a matter of great moment. Among other things, Shelburne had an extensive library of printed books (its sale some years later took a full month), numerous manuscripts, which were later purchased by the British Museum, and a unique personal collection of Italian marbles.

Priestley gave the matter a great deal of thought and asked his friends' advice. The salary offered was two and a half times what he was then receiving, and indeed seemed generous. It would bring considerable advantages for his family and would enable him to send his children to schools of his own choice, such as those run soon afterwards by the Barbaulds at Diss and by his former pupil, Estlin, at Bristol. On the other hand, he would not be completely free to do as he wished without considering Shelburne's interests and political aspirations; for it was possible that at any time he might be called upon to lead the government of the country.

Wedgwood thought it would be an excellent opportunity if Priestley was guaranteed freedom to write and act as he thought fit; otherwise he would be better employed at Leeds. Franklin was non-committal, but had a system for resolving complicated decisions; this was to write down all the arguments for and against in two columns, and cancel out items on both sides that seemed to carry equal weight. The column that survived this treatment the better would indicate where the choice lay.[1]

Priestley could not but appreciate Price's efforts on his behalf, but at first replied to the effect that if he ever did leave Leeds it would be for America. Nevertheless, he admitted that, counting ability and integrity together, Shelburne ranked as 'the very first character in this kingdom'. The turning-point came on a Saturday in August 1772 when Shelburne called on

---

[1] He called this 'Prudential Algebra'. Franklin to Price, 28 September 1772, in *Proc. Massachusetts Hist. Soc.*, 1903, *17* (2S), 363.

Priestley at Leeds and generously met every request he could make. He was to have a town house near Shelburne House in Berkeley Square, and a house on the Bowood estate at Calne, in Wiltshire. 'I shall launch into a new sphere of life about Christmas next,' he informed Price. As usual he would spend the winter months in London, and move to Calne in the summer.

But it was not until December 1772 that he finally decided to resign his pastoral office.[1] In doing this, he informed his congregation that he was in no way dissatisfied with conditions at Leeds. In reply, the congregation thanked him for his services. As parents, they particularly wished to give him their blessing 'for those affectionate and earnest endeavours which you have steadily pursued, in order to instil knowledge, and inculcate good principles on the minds of our children; and . . . we are desirous to bear our testimony, that as we received you in harmony and peace, so has love and friendship mutually prevailed between us, and we trust will ever prevail'.

On 16 May 1773 he at last preached his farewell sermon, and made a point of placing on record the happy associations he had enjoyed there, as the relations between pastor and people had been grossly misrepresented 'to serve the base purposes of a party'. Further, he said, 'I have been at full liberty to speak, write, or do, whatever I have judged that the interests of . . . christianity in general required. I do not know many congregations of dissenters in England, so numerous as that of Leeds, where I could have been so happy in this respect . . .'.

It had, indeed, been a remarkable association. A letter he wrote to Miss Aikin at Warrington when he was about to launch his most outspoken pamphlets shows that not every society would have appreciated his passion for free speech. 'I am about to make a bolder push than ever for the *pillory*, the *King's Bench Prison*, or something worse. Tell Mr Aikin he may hug himself that I have no connection with the Academy.'

Priestley's singleness of purpose and his wife's efficiency in the move from Leeds to Calne are to be seen in stories told by Mary

[1] Letter from J. Thornton to Lord Dartmouth, 22 January 1773: 'Your Lordp has probably heard that Lord Shelburne has engaged Dr Priestley of Leeds to come in March & be tutor to his sons . . .' (Hist. MSS. Comm., Rep. 14, App. X, vol. ii, 132).

Anne Galton, who in later years overheard much conversation between her mother and Mrs Priestley. But perhaps she listened to it when too young, and dictated it when too old, to be a reliable witness in every detail. Mrs Priestley, she said, packed everything for the long road journey; Priestley himself offered to help by fastening and roping the boxes. On their arrival Mrs Priestley opened them and found, under the cover of each box, a medley of minerals and mixtures of chemicals. Priestley begged her not to worry if the clothes were 'a little injured', for the other things had stood up to the journey perfectly well. On the day after their arrival, Mrs Priestley stood high on a pair of steps papering the walls with her own hands. Priestley was otherwise engaged among the boxes. Lord Shelburne arrived to welcome them, and Priestley hastily apologized for the state they were in. Mrs Priestley, however, remained calm. 'Lord Shelburne,' she said, 'is a statesman; and he knows that people are best employed in doing their duty.'

It was some time before they were settled in their new home. On 18 July Priestley, in a letter to William Turner at Wakefield, said they were still living in one room, as something or other required to be done in the others. His books were still in London; 'and I cannot be said to be settled till I have got to work at my experiments, or some thing else'. In the meantime he was writing additions to his *Essay on Education*. 'As Lord Shelburne is much interested in the observations, I shew them to him, and his friends. . . .' They were intended for publication, but nearly five years passed before he committed them to print.

The Priestleys lived at Calne as Shelburne's friends. On the whole their stay was a happy one, and a fourth child was born to them, called Henry at Shelburne's request. Neither of them attempted to take advantage of their situation for social ends, but even at times pointed out the benefit of belonging neither to the upper nor to the lower 'order'. On one occasion Shelburne gave Mrs Priestley a ticket to enable her to go to the trial of the Duchess of Kingston at the House of Lords. Elizabeth Chudleigh, formerly Countess of Bristol, had been pronounced a spinster by the courts in 1769, and she married the Duke of Kingston. In 1776, however, she was arraigned before the

House of Lords on a charge of bigamy. Mrs Priestley found that there was a rush for seats, much noise and trampling, and even clothes were torn. When Shelburne asked her how she had enjoyed the experience, she said: 'Indeed, my Lord, I find the conduct of the upper so exactly like that of the lower classes, that I was thankful I was born in middle life.'

Mrs Priestley was the mainstay of the Priestley household. She managed their children with affection and kindness, not unmixed with firmness. Mary Anne remembered her piercing eyes, and the sudden kindly smile—like the sun in January. But she also had the reputation of being a good conversationalist, and was highly praised as a correspondent.

Attending to the library and cataloguing the collections did not take much of Priestley's time, nor did the supervision of the education of his charges become onerous, as they already had a tutor. In the absence of a congregation to visit, he had little walking to do, and therefore took up gardening, partly for the exercise, but also to grow fresh vegetables. He occasionally preached on request at Calne, Devizes, and other places in the area. He remained as methodical as ever, allocating set periods for his various pursuits, and allowing time for relaxation. For example, he played three games of chess with his wife after dinner and another three after supper.

Apart from helping to entertain visitors to Bowood, he was free to carry on with his scientific work, for which Shelburne made him an additional allowance. In the winter months he left with Shelburne for London and served him in various capacities, conversing with his political and other guests, including visitors from overseas, and in arranging demonstrations of interesting new experiments. But even so his time was not fully taken up, and he was able to enjoy the society of his friends as never before.

With the help of Lee and Price, one of his first preoccupations was to see about the installation of Lindsey, who had come to London without any occupation, in the Unitarian hall they inaugurated in Essex Street. The first service was held on 17 April 1774, and among the congregation were Franklin and other notable people. At first there was some suspicion as to the true nature of the proceedings there, and a government agent attended the meetings until he was satisfied that they had no ulterior or unlawful significance. Lindsey was well connected and widely esteemed for the part he had played in the unsuccessful 'Feathers Tavern' petition to Parliament in 1771-2 for the relief of the universities from subscription to the 39 Articles; it was presented to the Commons on 6 February 1772 and, as mentioned previously, it had incurred the King's displeasure (p. 56). Priestley attended the services as often as he could, and sometimes delivered the sermon.

From time to time several influential people passed through the doors, though the average number was small; despite this, it became an important meeting-place for the diffusion of Unitarian thought and of liberal dissenting politics. Among those who are known to have attended often were Savile, Sir Thomas Brand, treasurer of the Foundling Hospital, Richard Kirwan, F.R.S. (one of Priestley's scientific intimates), Lee, Mrs Rayner, who became one of Priestley's most generous patrons, Mr Whitmore (the Member for Bridgnorth), and the Earl of Surrey. In later years Priestley and Lindsey made many other notable converts through their preaching and writings. They included the Duke of Grafton, a former prime minister and chancellor of Cambridge University at a time when the attempts to secure relief from subscription to the 39 Articles made the King decide to secure Lord North's appointment as chancellor of Oxford. Grafton later wrote Unitarian pamphlets and remained a supporter of Priestley in exile right to the last.

In the autumn of 1774 Priestley joined Shelburne in a tour of the Continent, from which he returned—according to Lindsey —a much improved man. He had been gratified to find that his reputation had preceded him, and that he was received everywhere with great respect. But also his outlook was widened, and he learnt much from seeing unfamiliar styles of architecture, observing other people's customs, and hearing other languages spoken. All the necessary arrangements were made for him, and he was free to enjoy his many conversations with members both of the political circles in which Shelburne moved, and of the literary and scientific world to which he gained entry in his own right.

Shelburne and Priestley travelled through Flanders and Holland and into Germany, and then returned via Strasbourg to Paris for about a month. Here Priestley made the acquaintance of Lavoisier and the chief figures in French science. Some of those he met had private laboratories, and he tried out certain experiments while he was there. What struck him most forcibly, however, was that no man of science seemed able to believe that his own scientific work had not destroyed his Christian faith. This discovery worried him, and led him afterwards to address certain pamphlets to 'philosophical unbelievers', in which he pointed out how unphilosophical it was to reject all the historical evidences of Christianity without proper examination. It was foolish to maintain, as some seemed to imagine, that Christianity had been introduced by the civil authorities as a means of holding the people in subjection, for it was historical fact that Christianity had grown up in countries where the civil authorities had done everything in their power to suppress it.

While Shelburne and Priestley were in Paris an event occurred that undoubtedly took the French people a step nearer to the Revolution. Until 1771 the Royal courts of law, or the *parlements*, in Paris and the provinces had been one of the few surviving relics of the medieval French constitution.[1] In 1771 the Paris court of law had been 'exiled' by Louis XV and its functions were made over to the *Conseil d'État*. After this he had done all he could to abolish the *parlements* altogether, and with them the right of a privileged class to purchase what amounted almost to immunity from taxation. With the aid of his chief ministers other financial reforms were attempted. In May 1774 the King died, and his successor, Louis XVI, together with Marie Antoinette, set about forthwith to undo these reforms. Two of the chief ministers lost their offices in August that year, and on 27 October the *parlements* were re-established. One other old practice was revived. If the *parlements* of former days had resisted the King's decrees and refused to register them, he could override them by the procedure known as the *lit de justice*, which took its name from the throne of four cushions

[1] A. Cobban, 'The Parlements of France in the eighteenth century', *History*, 1950, *35*, 64–80.

of blue velvet decorated with the *fleur de lys* on which the King sat. Louis XVI arranged such a function to coincide with the restoration of the Paris *parlement* early in November.

Priestley said that he tired of Parisian society and decided to return before Shelburne. But it may be that this restitution of ancient privilege in Paris, which few really expected to lead to the fair administration of justice, was displeasing to him. On the other hand, the pomp of a state occasion appealed to Shelburne, and he stayed on for about ten days especially to see the *lit de justice*. Priestley arrived in London on the evening of 2 November, and the following day was busy on Shelburne's business, interviewing Colonel Barré and others of his political followers.

The tour had interested Priestley immensely, and he spent the first evening after his return telling Lindsey of his experiences. Writing to their mutual friend Turner to inform him of Priestley's arrival, Lindsey said: 'I leave the Doctor to give you a long list of 1000 things his curious mind has picked up. One thing I will venture to say, that he is much improved by this view of mankind at large. . . .'

Many years afterwards, referring to this period of his life, Priestley said that he daily saw and conversed with the leading politicians of Great Britain and all parts of Europe. He mentioned his connection with such men as Turgot, the first controller-general of the new regime in France, and his successor Necker, whose attempts at reform were frustrated by the power that had been put back into the hands of the privileged classes. The duc de la Rochefoucauld d'Enville, he said, was a constant correspondent from the time of his visit to France.

In view of this, it is difficult to believe that Priestley was not concerned with politics during his stay with Shelburne. If Priestley's son Joseph had allowed his father's political correspondence to be published, instead of suppressing it, we should find it much easier to get at the truth of this matter.

One important letter, which seems to have been overlooked, shows that Priestley sometimes went even further than his duties to Shelburne demanded. In 1775 he tried to enlist support for Shelburne from Savile and his friends among the Rockingham Whigs. On 28 October he wrote to Savile about

Shelburne's 'real wishes and views with respect to the present posture of affairs'. He went on: [1]

> I think I may venture to say that I know Lord Shelburne very well, and I would be far from leading Sir George Savile into a mistake with respect to him. He is by no means that artful ambitious politician that he has been represented, and he is far from wishing to draw you from any connection you may have with the Marquis of Rockingham and his friends; so far from it, that he would himself most cordially act with, and even *under*, the Marquis (for so I have heard him express himself many times), provided his measures were more distinct and decisive, going to the bottom of the present disorders of the State. And all he wishes with respect to you is, that, as he thinks you are naturally more disposed in favour of what is manly and decisive, you would use your influence with the Marquis of Rockingham and his connections, to induce them to adopt such measures.

So much for the suspicions that many held as to Shelburne's motives—suspicions that led him to be known as Malagrida, or the ' Jesuit of Berkeley Square'.

> Lord Shelburne is not without that prudence and circumspection that becomes his situation, but he has no deep political secrets. What he avowedly wishes is, when the times are a little more ripe to bear the proposal, that the power of the Crown should be abridged, especially with respect to the disposal of the Revenue, and that a thorough enquiry be made into the source of the present wretched Administration, and proper examples be made. I believe he will never be brought cordially to acquiesce in anything that he shall think to be less effectual remedies than these.

With prophetic insight he saw Shelburne as the most likely of the more liberal politicians to be able to negotiate an acceptable settlement with America.

> With regard to America, I cannot help thinking that the people of that country would have more confidence in Lord Shelburne, provided there should ever be an opening to treat with them (which, however, for my own part, I despair of), than in Lord Rockingham, whose *declaratory Act* will never go down with them.

So often were Priestley's own political motives to be mis-

[1] Hist. MSS. Comm., Rep. 15, App., Pt. V, 149. This has since been noticed by J. Norris, *Shelburne and Reform*, London, 1963, 100.

represented in future years, that the concluding paragraph of this letter should also be reproduced.

I know Lord Shelburne wishes to explain himself to you upon these subjects, and would have no objection to do it in the presence of Lord Rockingham, or any of his friends. You will find him frank, plain, and open, like yourself; and I shall think myself happy if I should be the means of bringing about such an interview as would give an opportunity of a free and unreserved communication of your sentiments, and might lead men who equally wish well to the State to act in concert for its good. Be the issue what it may, I shall be easier for having written to you to this purpose. Your own discretion must do the rest.

Savile received the note at his house in Leicester Fields, and, though unwell at the time, replied the following day. The letter shows Savile's great respect, not only for Shelburne, but for Priestley also. Priestley was right in thinking there was common ground between them, for Savile said:

It has been for many years matter of great concern to me to observe that the even very moderate number of persons who seemed to me to entertain the most just and constitutional principles were rendered still less effective by being again subdivided amongst themselves, and so rendered less respectable than even a Minority need be, and it is now indeed a good while since I had given almost over all hopes of ever seeing it otherwise. Nothing could make me more happy than to find myself mistaken, and nothing so proud as being in any degree instrumental in bringing about so very desirable an event. I do assure you, were you a minister, you could offer me no contract, no job, that I should catch at so eagerly as that of which you give me the preference, but I do not feel that I have any powers to do it . . .

Even in more able hands than Savile's it was unlikely that the very divided opposition to Lord North's ministry could be unified and thus strengthened, and Savile was pessimistic about the result of any approaches. However, he arranged to see Priestley forthwith and before showing the letter to anyone else. Unfortunately, there seems to be no record of the outcome of this approach.

Despite the busy periods in the previous two years, Priestley had found time to carry out more original researches, and had made several sets of discoveries, any one of which would have ensured that his name would be remembered in the history of chemistry. He had prepared and studied the properties of alkaline air (ammonia), an acid air from vitriolic acid (sulphur dioxide), an air later known as nitrous oxide, and—most important of all—he had isolated oxygen in August 1774, and carried out a series of researches upon it in the spring of 1775. He now had a large repertory of new experiments to show at Shelburne House.

At this time Bentley, who was living over the new Wedgwood showrooms in Greek Street, Soho, was a frequent visitor, as also was Wedgwood himself when in town. They had much to talk about. Bentley followed all aspects of Priestley's work with enthusiasm, and passed on the details to other interested people, such as Warltire, who showed the experiments in his lectures. Another matter in which they were all concerned was the Grand Trunk Navigation, which was nearing completion. In 1766 Bentley had spent six months in London in connection with the Bill authorizing the work on the canal which passed through Wedgwood's pottery works at Etruria, opened in 1769. They prophesied an immense expansion of trade when Liverpool became the chief outlet for the manufactured goods of the Midlands.

These three friends were also acquainted with several of those who frequented the Slaughter's Club meetings not far from Wedgwood's showrooms. They included Joseph Banks, Captain Cook, Dr Templeman (Secretary of the Society of Arts), John Smeaton (who had made Priestley's air-pump), Dr George Fordyce, and Richard Lovell Edgeworth; most of these were liberal-minded men who respected Priestley. Fordyce, however, was representative of another group, for in 1774 he had been admitted a member of Samuel Johnson's literary club. Johnson was also acquainted with various other medical and scientific men, including the Irishman, Bryan Higgins, and Richard Brocklesby, who became his physician. From this quarter Priestley received an attack that proved a very bitter experience to him, and to which he responded in a manner that silenced his adversaries but was scarcely calculated to gain them as friends.

This unpleasant episode illustrates the involved state of affairs at that period, when men who could combine on one issue often found themselves in opposing camps on others. Though Boswell, like Johnson, disliked 'Whiggish democratical notions', he took exception to Johnson's pamphlet on the question of American taxation, written early in 1775 for the administration. 'Positive assertion, sarcastical severity, and extravagant ridicule, which he himself reprobated as a test of truth, were united in this rhapsody,' said Boswell. All that the Chatham Whigs, and Franklin, Priestley, and their friends stood for was attacked and decried. And it was an Anglican, Samuel Parr, who complained that Johnson had derided Priestley's sect too coarsely and too indiscriminately. Lord North, in his capacity as chancellor of Oxford, chose this moment to recognize Johnson's merit by conferring upon him the degree of Doctor in Civil Law.

At about the same time Brocklesby and Higgins attacked Priestley's scientific reputation, and the criticism appears to have influenced Fordyce and Bentham as well. Higgins was a physician, practical chemist, and lecturer on chemistry at his house in Greek Street, and Priestley, in the early months of 1775, found it convenient to call on him to obtain certain chemical preparations for his experiments. In May Priestley invited Higgins and Brocklesby to Shelburne House and demonstrated some of his latest discoveries, including the more remarkable properties of oxygen. Afterwards they spread a rumour to the effect that these experiments were not new and had been shown for some time past at Higgins's lectures. Priestley had in fact begun to attend one of Higgins's courses in the spring, but he had not been impressed with his understanding of gas manipulations. The allegations spread around the clubs, and quickly came to Priestley's ears. At first he took little notice, but the story appeared to gain ground, and his friends warned him that he should take action to stop it.

Higgins, when challenged, added to the charge of plagiarism, and said that Priestley's originality consisted chiefly in the knack of 'rendering the phenomena, which all practical chemists have observed and understood, perfectly mysterious and surprising to others'. It appears therefore that Higgins had not given very close attention to Priestley's writings and experimental work, or else that he had an ulterior motive in trying to depreciate the value of this work. As there seemed little hope of persuading him to withdraw his allegations, Priestley decided to demolish the charge of plagiarism once and for all. This he did in his *Philosophical Empiricism* (1775). It might be thought that at most a few pages would have been enough, but Priestley discussed the matter in great detail and made it a fair-sized book. Circumstances may have justified this outburst, and there is no record that any of his friends objected to it. But at few other times in history would this kind of wrangling between men of science have passed without comment. Perhaps the most interesting part of the book is that in which Priestley gave his own view of his function in science.

It may be my fate to be a kind of comet, or flaming meteor in science, in the regions of which (like enough to a meteor) I made my appearance very lately, and very unexpectedly; and therefore, like a meteor, it may be my destiny to move very swiftly, burn away with great heat and violence, and become as suddenly extinct.

But he warned Higgins to keep out of the way of his tail— in the event a much longer one than he seems to have expected. In this unprofitable dispute Brocklesby was let off lightly, owing to his attachment to the cause of liberty.

Judging by Bentham's account, Fordyce also incurred Priestley's displeasure. Bentham said in conversation that Priestley annoyed him by treating Fordyce as an ignorant man.

Now I worshipped Dr. Fordyce on account of his chemical knowledge. He knew every thing that was known. Dr. Priestley assumed he had made discoveries, which were no discoveries.

As an example Bentham cited marine acid air, known, he said, for centuries. But it is doubtful if Bentham's knowledge of chemistry at this time was very advanced, despite his keenness on the subject,[1] and Fordyce himself does not cut a very impressive figure in the pages of either Bentham, Boswell, or Samuel Rogers. Boswell showed him being defeated by Johnson

---

[1] University College, London, Bentham Papers, Box 107—1 contains papers touching on gases and heat, dated 7 and 8 April, probably when Bentham was a pupil of Fordyce. Another paper, probably 1774, mentions several gases including nitrous air.

on his own ground. Nevertheless Fordyce was well known as a writer on diverse medical and scientific topics and became a F.R.S. in 1776. He also gave courses of lectures on chemistry; but Bentham knew him first at an unfortunate time, when his laboratory had been damaged by fire and he had been reduced to demonstrating with a small portable furnace and a few flasks and 'common things'.

Bentham was not quite fair to Priestley, for he did not say that he had been in correspondence with him at Calne, and had received a civil though not altogether approving reply in connection with a new method of preparing airs which Bentham had outlined, without saying who the author was. In his answer of 16 December 1774 Priestley said that he had no objection to the method except that it 'must be rather troublesome in practice'. As regards the use of nitrous air for comparing the goodness of specimens of common air, Priestley thought it unnecessary to worry much about the purity of the nitrous air, provided it was taken from the same jar for all the measurements. 'Besides, by losing a little of the first produce of nitrous, or any other kind of air, you may be certain of having it very pure.'

In the same letter Bentham had tackled Priestley about the names he had given to his acid air, which he had since qualified with the epithet of marine. Priestley said that at first he did not want to make the term more complicated than necessary, but he had since 'produced the other acid airs, with great variations'; accordingly, in the new edition of his treatise on air (1775), he had given the first acid air a more precise name.

I have made very considerable additions to my observations on air, and am not determined whether to send an account of them to the Royal Society or make a *supplement* to my book; but I rather think I shall do the latter.

Bentham had also sent Priestley a paper on electricity, in which the author had set out to prove that lightning was caused by the friction of clouds. Priestley said he liked the ingenuity the author had shown; 'but he will excuse me if I observe, that I find no sufficient *friction* to produce electricity in the manner that he supposes. The motion that is perceived in small clouds during a thunderstorm seems to me to be the *effect* of preceding electricity.'

He ended by saying: 'I expect to be in London soon after Christmas, and then shall hope to have the pleasure of an interview with you . . .'

Priestley adopted a similar critical attitude towards Higgins's lecture experiments, emphasizing the importance of simple apparatus. Higgins seemed to think that a substance like alkaline air required a vacuum in which to expand in order to become permanently elastic. So he used very long tubes, with the result that some of his demonstrations did not 'succeed to his wish'. Priestley and Higgins also had different ideas about fixed air and phlogisticated air. Priestley had proved that the purer the air was the greater its specific gravity, but Higgins said that 'phlogisticated air does not greatly exceed pure air in specific gravity'. This, Priestley said, was Rutherford's idea, and apparently his professor, William Cullen, thought so too. They could be pardoned, as the subject had not then been fully investigated. But now there could be no excuse. He again pointed out how the two airs differed, and said that the difference in specific gravity was decisive.

Priestley thought Higgins might be a good chemist, but not much of a philosopher, by which he meant that he was more skilled in routine preparations than in research. Priestley often admitted his own lack of expertise in such matters, and that was the reason why he went to men like Higgins, Peter Woulfe, and Cavendish for practical hints.

At this time Priestley thought that chemistry was insufficiently advanced for any pronouncements to be made about the 'primary constituent parts' of substances. Despite this, he had a full share of 'curiosity, and such a desire of knowledge, as misled our first parents', to have given thought to the question. To Priestley any theory of matter had to apply to the whole of creation. He thus tended towards the views of Father Boscovich and Michell, which he had outlined in his history of optics, thinking that they threw much light on the 'constituent principles of human nature'. Man was composed of the same matter as the rest of nature, and it seemed to follow that perception and mental powers were not the properties of matter as such, but the result of the brain's structure. Thus at death the 'whole man' ceased to exist; and his hope of immortality could be based only on Christian revelation. In this he thought of himself less as a scientist than as one trying to complete the work begun by the Reformers and whose duty it was to combat every belief that would not stand up to the test of reason. If Christianity was to survive the attacks of scientists and unbelievers, certain concepts would have to be given up. One of these was 'the notion of a soul'. He hoped that materialism, in the sense that man is a wholly material being, would become a firm tenet of rational Christians.[1]

Little reliance, he thought, could be placed on any theory of the 'internal structure of matter', as there were few data to argue from.[2] It could certainly be argued that *solid* atoms were impossible, for in nature there is no real or absolute contact between bodies, and from this it appeared that the resistance at the centre of a particle or at a physical point becomes infinite. With Boscovich, therefore, he thought it more likely that matter consisted of physical points endowed with spheres of attraction and repulsion. Thus matter might be infinitely divisible, although consisting of individual particles. His thinking never left the practical plane of everyday life, and sometimes he brings us back sharply with striking examples:

What peculiar excellence is there in those particles of matter which compose my body, more than those which compose the table on which I write . . . If I knew that they were instantly, and without any painful sensation to myself, to change places, I do not think it would give me any concern.

A good example of the way in which everything Priestley did in one field bore on what he was doing in others is to be seen

---

[1] This led to an 'epitaph', attributed to the Rev. David Davis, a prominent schoolmaster in Wales (*Notes & Queries*, 1874, 2 (5S), 126).

> 'Here lie at rest
> In oaken chest,
> Together packed most nicely,
> The bones and brains,
> Flesh, blood, and veins,
> And *soul* of Dr. Priestley.'

[2] Dr R. E. Schofield has since given an interesting account in *J. Hist. Ideas*, 1964, 25(2), 285–94.

in the way he related the idea of the soul to that of gas and spirit in chemistry. The unknown thing over a fermenting liquor that caused the death of animals or the bursting of casks was first called a *gas* or the *spirit of the liquor*. The fermented liquor itself, possessing very active powers, was thought to contain *another kind of spirit* (spirit of wine). Some were still happy to call the air or any *invisible fluid* concerned in an experiment by the old name of spirit. This was not good enough, he thought, and so, to avoid introducing any new terms, he had kept to the term airs, already used by many scientists from Boyle onwards. Human beings associated life with breath, and hence in Hebrew, Greek, and Latin the word for *soul* was the same as that for *breath*. (In this paraphrase, Priestley's italics have been kept.) Just as the material view of invisible fluids made the idea of spirits unnecessary in chemistry, so he thought the idea of the soul should now be dropped.

By the summer of 1777 his *Disquisitions relating to Matter and Spirit* was ready for the printer. This was the second time he had tentatively suggested that the notion of the soul was superfluous. On the first occasion, he said, 'the cry against me as an unbeliever, and a favourer of atheism, was exceedingly general and loud . . . with what intention is best known to the authors of such gross defamation'.

This book, he later admitted, narrowed the circle of his friends. Some people, indeed, made political capital out of it, as he had already been warned might happen. Lindsey went with him the whole way with his latest ideas, but Price could not, and this led the two friends into a public controversy. The debate was conducted with politeness and mutual respect, and was held out to the world as an example of how serious matters should be discussed without acrimony and without loss of mutual esteem.

But the *Disquisitions* was only one of three books that were published within a short while of each other. The first was his *Course of Lectures on Oratory and Criticism*, which he had given at Warrington in 1762 and later years. This was dedicated to his patron's son, Lord Fitzmaurice. A further edition of his essay on education was required, and he now added the new material he had composed at Bowood. This was finished by the end of

SOPHIA,
DAUGHTER
OF JOHN AND SOPHIA EARL AND COUNTESS GRANVILLE,
WIFE
OF WILLIAM EARL OF SHELBURNE, BARON WYCOMBE
MOTHER
OF JOHN-HENRY VISCOUNT FITZ-MAURICE
AND WILLIAM GRANVILLE PETTY,
DIED IN THE TWENTY-SIXTH YEAR OF HER AGE,
ON THE SIXTH OF JANUARY, MDCCLXXI.

HER PRICE WAS FAR ABOVE RUBIES.
HER CHILDREN . RISE UP, AND CALL HER BLESSED
HER HUSBAND . ALSO, AND HE PRAISETH HER
SOLOMON.

Plate 11 One of Priestley's duties was to supervise the education of Shelburne's sons, here shown with their mother Sophia, daughter of Earl Granville. She had died in 1771, and this monument was erected by Shelburne in the Parish Church, High Wycombe. (*R. Simmons*)

Plate 12 Joseph Priestley at the height of his career. From the original portrait by Henry Fuseli, later a professor at the Royal Academy. This portrait was said to be a good likeness, though the features are a little exaggerated. (*Dr Williams's Library*)

1777 and printed at Bath in 1778; Lindsey thought it would prove most useful to the public and to posterity. In this new material, he made a strong plea for the wider study of science among those with time and money at their disposal, as well as among the young—the younger the better. This would help them to realize that science was a rational, useful, and honourable pursuit, and not merely a particular species of amusement.

Meanwhile there were signs of increasing political activity among the Whigs, and two minor victories were soon to be won for the Dissenters. Both were of considerable interest to him. In 1778 Savile introduced the Bill that removed some of the worst and most oppressive of the regulations against Catholics provided they denied certain doctrines subversive to the State. Legally, the saying of mass by a foreigner was still a felony and by a native was high treason. One of the last to be arrested on such a pretext was J. H. de Magalhaens (Magellan), F.R.S., a Portuguese resident in England, and one of Priestley's chief links with the Continent.[1] He became a visitor to Bowood where he wrote a booklet on domestic machines for making aerated waters and on eudiometers (p. 77). The suit in which Magellan was involved was heard before Lord Mansfield, but was dismissed on a legal technicality.

The success of Savile's Bill opened the way for a further application of the Dissenters in 1779, whose previous efforts (in 1772 and again in 1774) had been abortive. In view of this, it is not without interest that Priestley appears to have tried to obtain an audience with the King in February 1779. Other scholars had achieved this by applying to use the King's library. What Priestley's object was is not clear, but it seems unlikely that he merely wished to consult the books there. The approach was made through William Eden and Lord North, but the King made his position quite clear.[2] In a note to North headed 'Queen's House, 33 min. past 5 p.m., Feb. 22, 1779', he wrote:

If Dr Priestley applies to my librarian, he will have permission to see the library as other men of science have had: but I cannot think the Doctor's character as a politician or divine deserves my appear-

[1] Letters illustrating Magellan's role will be found in British Museum, Add. MSS. 28539, 33977, and 35126.
[2] B. Dobrée (Ed.), *The Letters of King George III*, London, 1935, 139.

ing at all in it: instruments I have none in London. I am sorry
Mr. Eden has any intimacy with that Doctor, as I am not over-fond
of those that frequent any disciples or companions of the Jesuit in
Berkeley Square.

The new-won relief for the Dissenters did not go far, but it did
allow dissenting clergymen and schoolmasters to exercise their
religion and practice their profession without being molested.

Later that year the situation generally deteriorated. Many
political associations were being formed in various parts of the
country, and in these several of Priestley's friends were working
actively.[1] On 30 December 1779, at a county meeting at York,
a petition was drawn up, with 9,000 signatures, and Savile was
charged with the duty of presenting it to the House of Commons,
which he did on 8 February 1780. It contained such familiar
expressions as: 'the true end of every legitimate government is
. . . the welfare of the community'. It called among other
things for a cessation of gross expenditure of public money on
unmerited pensions, exorbitant emoluments, and sinecures. Its
clear object was to check the power of the Crown. On the same
day Shelburne, in the Lords, called for an inquiry into the
expenditure of public money. On 11 February Burke produced
his economic plan for rectifying financial abuses. On 21 February Savile moved for a list of the pensions. North intervened
with an amendment to restrict the list to those paid by the
Exchequer, thus excluding any public inquiry into the King's
use of public funds for his own political ends. This amendment,
as Fox said, would mean divulging only a 'trifling part of the
enormous list'. The fight was on; but the amendment was
carried by 188 votes to 186. It seemed that persistence would
win the day. In March the Yorkshire Association echoed the
cry heard in several parts of the country that as the influence
of the Crown was being exerted to destroy the independence of
Parliament, that influence should be limited. On 6 April John
Dunning, one of Shelburne's followers, succeeded in getting his
two celebrated motions passed by the Commons:

(1) That it is necessary to declare, that the influence of the Crown
has increased, is increasing, and ought to be diminished; and

[1] See Rev. Christopher Wyvill, *Political Papers* . . ., 6 vols., 1794–?1806.

(2) That it is competent to this House, to examine into, and to correct, abuses in the expenditure of the Civil List Revenues, as well as in every other branch of the Public Revenue, whenever it shall appear expedient to the wisdom of this House so to do.[1]

This established a principle, but it implied no further action at that stage. Before matters could be taken to a conclusion, parliamentary business was interrupted in June by the mob that rose under Lord George Gordon's instigation in protest against the relief granted to Catholics two years earlier. Savile was one of the main objects of their wrath, and he had to be given military protection for some days. North was treated with little more respect.

After this no immediate progress was made, and Savile, on 5 September, told his constituents that he had become a 'poor, barren, ineffectual negative'. He was baffled and dispirited by the turn of events, 'with hardly a ray of hope of seeing any change in the miserable course of public calamities'. With affairs in this unsettled state, Priestley had already learnt (through Price) that Shelburne was thinking of setting him up on one of his estates in Ireland. This he took as a hint that Shelburne would have no objection to ending their association. He seems to have been in a sensitive frame of mind, and a later Lord Fitzmaurice could discover no evidence to explain why Priestley decided to leave. He asked Shelburne if he had done anything wrong, and was assured that he had not. Many suggestions have been offered since, but it appears that Priestley left for no other reason than that he thought it right to do so. For more than four years he had been hinting in his writings that his work in science might have been finished, and that he strongly felt the call of religion, philosophy, and metaphysics.[2] There remained many things for him to do, and he may have felt that he could not do them while connected too intimately with a politician of Shelburne's standing.

If it had been true that Priestley had political ambitions of

---

[1] *Journals of the House of Commons.*

[2] Shelburne sided with Price on religious questions, rather than with Priestley. On 19 December 1786 Shelburne said to Price that if Priestley decided to form a sect he could only call them 'atheistical Christians, men who would not believe in a God if it was not for Jesus Christ' (*Proc. Massachusetts Hist. Soc.*, 1903, *17* (2S), 363).

his own, as some had been hinting, now surely would have been the time to stay close to Shelburne and Savile—menwith whose views he could well associate himself. He chose not to; and this in itself strongly vindicates the independent character of one who took little thought for the morrow.

Chapter 8

Acids and Alkalis

IN 1787, at Lindsey's request, Kirwan wrote a short apprecia-
tion of Priestley's work from 1772 onwards.

How many invisible fluids, whose existence evaded the sagacity of
former ages, has he made known to us? The very air we breathe, he
has taught us to analyze, to examine, to improve: a substance so little
known, that even the precise effect of respiration was an enigma until
he explained it. He first made known the proper food of vegetables,
and in what the difference between these and animal substances consisted. To him pharmacy is indebted for the method of making artificial mineral waters, as well as for the shorter method of preparing
other medicines; metallurgy, for more powerful and cheaper solvents;
and chemistry for . . . discoveries, which have new modelled that
science, and drawn to it, and to this country, the attention of all
Europe.

In this short account most of the things for which Priestley is
remembered are mentioned. But one item may surprise even
those who have already read about his work—the debt owed
to him by metallurgy for more powerful and cheaper solvents,
mainly the mineral acids. Priestley's studies of acids were indeed
very extensive, and led to valuable practical results.

By the time Priestley received the Copley Medal his work on
airs had gone so far and so fast that Sir John Pringle agreed
that it would be better to print his results in book form rather
than send lengthy papers to the Royal Society, which might be
subject to delays in publication. When he moved to Calne in
the summer of 1773 he had with him sufficient material for one
such book, and by the time he left in 1780 he had accumulated
enough for four more. Thus five of the six volumes on which
his fame chiefly rests were written before he left Shelburne's
service. To one who shared the family name of Petty with one

of the Royal Society's most illustrious founders, this must have seemed ample recompense for his patronage.

Priestley's first three volumes, with the title *Experiments and Observations on different Kinds of Air*, were published in 1774, 1775, and 1777. (Second editions of the first two volumes were required in 1775 and 1776 respectively.) By that time his interests had broadened and the discovery of new airs was no longer his chief aim. The title of the fourth volume (1779) was therefore changed to *Experiments and Observations relating to various Branches of Natural Philosophy* . . ., and this was retained for the second (1781) and third (1786) volumes of the new series. Kirwan thus had all six in mind when he wrote his note for Lindsey.

Alkaline Air

Priestley had been impressed by the ease with which chemical actions could be followed with the acid air from spirit of salt, and this prompted him to try similar experiments with other acids and alkalis. He began in 1773 by trying to obtain the fumes of the volatile alkali (ammonia) as an air. This led to new findings in quick succession, and it demonstrated his mastery of the technique of studying substances in the form of 'air'.

He took some 'volatile spirit of sal ammoniac' (ammonia solution) and heated it with a candle, as he had done the spirit of salt, collecting the air over mercury. He then obtained the same air from spirit of hartshorn and sal volatile. From the last he obtained fixed air as well. The two airs, indeed, united again in the delivery tube (as had been demonstrated by Black several years earlier), blocking it and bursting the vessels. After trials, he found that the best way of making the alkaline air was to heat a mixture of sal ammoniac (ammonium chloride) and quicklime. Then it was contaminated only with water, also produced in the reaction, and he found an easy way of removing this by inserting a trap in the delivery tube (Plate 9).

Having mastered the preparation, Priestley decided to try whether alkaline air and acid air would unite to form a neutral air. The moment they came together, he said, a beautiful white cloud was formed, which soon filled the whole vessel. They had united to form a white salt, which he examined and found to be sal ammoniac. He had now found a way of demonstrating the presence of acid in an air; so he repeated the experiment with nitrous air, and promptly obtained a white cloud. Was there any acid in common air? He tried it, but it had no effect.

Sponge, linen, and charcoal, he found, seemed to 'condense' the alkaline air on their surfaces, as when pieces of these materials were taken out of the vessel the smell was so pungent as to be 'almost intolerable'. Alkaline air, he discovered, was slightly inflammable, burning with a yellowish flame. The electric spark appeared red—the same as with Cavendish's inflammable air—but it was not until 1775 that, by continuous sparking, he noticed a considerable increase in volume; after dissolving as much of the produce as possible in water, he found that the remainder was indeed inflammable air. But he could not explain this.

His method of preparing alkaline air from sal ammoniac and quicklime, with the use of a water-trap, has remained the standard preparation. By this time he had also found that the marine acid air could best be obtained by heating oil of vitriol with common salt, and this, too, remained the standard method. Other preparations, which are still those of the textbooks, were to follow.

Nitrous and Similar Airs

A different air from any he had known was obtained when a large surface of iron was exposed to nitrous air to see if it would rust. Other experimenters would have watched the iron, but it seems that Priestley forgot all about it, and concentrated on the change in the nitrous air. Instead of finding the usual symptoms of 'phlogistication', namely phlogisticated air, he discovered that it was changed to a new species of air that he would have formerly considered impossible—candles burned quite naturally in it, and yet the air was highly noxious to animals. Still longer exposure to iron gave 'air' (nitrous oxide) in which a candle burned with an *enlarged* flame. After shaking it with water to remove any soluble air, Priestley found that the remainder (nitrogen) extinguished a flame and was noxious.

From this he deduced that nitrous air and this phlogisticated nitrous air were composed of the same two ingredients but had a different mode of combination, or a different proportion of the ingredients in their composition. This very suggestive statement, as it happened, was some years ahead of its time, and later workers received the credit for carrying out the suggested analysis. But he gave a broad enough hint. He thought that 'by a little more attention to these experiments, the whole mystery of this proportion and combination may be explained'.

Vitriolic Acid Air

In the summer of 1774 Priestley tried to do the same with vitriolic acid as he had done with the marine acid (spirit of salt). He knew there was a form of sulphuric acid (now termed sulphurous acid) that gave off strong-smelling fumes, and he thought that would serve his purpose. However, not being expert in chemical preparations he was unable to make it for himself, and he could find no one in Wiltshire who understood what he wanted. In the autumn he was a visitor with Shelburne at the seat of Monsieur Trudaine at Montigny where he had 'a complete apparatus of philosophical instruments, with every other convenience and assistance for pursuing such philosophical enquiries as any of his numerous guests shall chuse to entertain themselves with'. There he met Étienne Mignot de Montigny, a member of the Academy of Sciences and a nephew of Voltaire, and together they tried to make some 'volatile vitriolic acid' by boiling oil of vitriol in a cracked phial with a pan of charcoal. This did not prove successful, and they heated the vitriol with turpentine. There was a sudden rush of 'air' that overturned the receiver, and so they desisted, scarcely thinking a host's house the right place for risky affairs of that kind. After his return, Priestley, on 26 November, tried the experiment again. Beginning with olive oil and oil of vitriol, he immediately found the air he wanted—so much of it, indeed, that the cork blew out of the phial and the contents exploded. He was surrounded by white smoke, and the air had a choking smell (sulphur trioxide and sulphur dioxide, respectively). Afterwards he tried charcoal instead of olive oil, and obtained a much smoother reaction, which permitted collection of the air over mercury without danger.

This 'manner of producing air from substances contained in small phials, and receiving the produce in quicksilver, when it is of such a nature that it cannot be confined by water, has never failed to strike every person to whom I have shewed it', he said.

This air combined readily with water, and 'must have formed the volatile or sulphureous acid of vitriol. Indeed the result of this combination was so obvious, that I did not think it necessary to make the experiment.' When he mixed the air with alkaline air, he obtained a very beautiful white cloud, which rose to the top of the vessel, showing that alkaline air was the lighter of the two. By analogy with marine acid air, he concluded that the product was vitriolic sal ammoniac (ammonium sulphate), but again he felt so sure that he did not test it. This time he was not quite right. When vitriolic acid air was left for some time in common air, the goodness of the latter was reduced. Charcoal absorbed this acid air and acquired a very pungent smell.

He then tried to obtain the same air with the aid of a number of other 'phlogistic' materials. The simplest method of preparation, which became the standard school method, would by Priestley have been called an accidental discovery, though he did much hard work before he arrived at it. He was trying to obtain the white fumes given off when oil of vitriol was heated strongly by itself, but they condensed on reaching the cooler part of the phial. Some mercury ran back into the acid, and 'a prodigious quantity of air was generated, the tube through which it was transmitted was broken into many pieces . . . and part of the hot acid being spilled upon my hand, burned it terribly, so that the effect of it is visible to this day. The inside of the phial was coated with a white saline substance, and the smell that issued from it was extremely suffocating.'

Despite the mishap and the pain, he was back at work on the following day, and obtained the gas readily by gently heating a little mercury with the acid. He then repeated it with other metals, looking out carefully for inflammable air, which would have been obtained if the acid were diluted. Zinc gave two-thirds and iron wire one-third of inflammable air; copper and silver gave all acid air. With gold, and a specimen of platinum he was given by Irving, there was no action. This kind of work, so important for future experimenters who wished to obtain pure samples of gases, is an aspect of his studies for which he has seldom been given sufficient credit.

Fluor Acid Air

Priestley now turned to the new mineral acid that had been discovered by Scheele in Sweden by the action of oil of vitriol on fluorspar. The new acid (hydrofluoric acid mixed with silicon tetrafluoride) was usually prepared by distillation from glass vessels, which became corroded in the process. If there was any water in the reservoir it became coated with a crust, which Scheele found to be 'quartz' (silica).

At first Priestley had no idea as to the nature of the material Scheele had used, and so he asked Peter Woulfe, who gave him a specimen of fluorspar from Saxony. Priestley soon found that Derbyshire spar was just as satisfactory. This was of much interest, for Derbyshire spar was used widely for making vases and other chimney ornaments, and he had been given several pieces of scrap by Matthew Boulton when on an earlier visit to his works at Soho, Birmingham.

Instead of distilling the mixture of fluorspar and acid into a receiver, Priestley collected the product as air (silicon tetrafluoride) over mercury. As soon as water was admitted a crust formed, and this gradually moved up the side as it accumulated; eventually all the watery layer turned to a stiff jelly (silica gel). He took the jelly out and pressed it, obtaining a strongly acid liquor and an earth. He therefore considered that the air was a compound of acid and earth, and termed it fluor acid air. With alkaline air it formed a white cloud, but slowly, producing a salt and the same stony substance.

This stony substance, being mixed [combined] with the acid air, is also probably the reason why the alkaline air does not mix so readily with it as with the other kinds of acid air; some time being requisite to disengage it from this stony substance, in order to its uniting with the alkaline air.

By heating a strong solution of the acid he obtained the air from it (hydrogen fluoride) and by every test he had at his disposal he found the same results as with vitriolic acid air. When he heated it strongly in glass, the stony matter again appeared, but he did not realize that in this case it had come from the glass. He tasted the acid, and said that it was astringent, like alum.

Red Nitrous Vapour

Priestley's attempts to study what he called 'nitrous acid vapour itself' (p. 97) led to many interesting observations. He filled a bottle with the red vapour by simple displacement of the air, and noticed that it stayed red indefinitely if the bottle was closely stoppered. He then studied the effect of heat on the gas by sealing some in a glass tube of length 3 feet and diameter 1 inch. When he held the tube in his hand the air at that end of the tube became noticeably deeper in colour. On holding it to the fire, the heated end went intensely red. When cold the same gas was nearly colourless. This so intrigued him and his friends that for a time a small phial filled with the red air was always to be found in his pocket. (Later he obtained the air by heating solid lead nitrate in a tube, sealing off the tube just above the solid that was being heated.)

Thinking that the red vapour was spirit of nitre deprived of its water, he began a series of experiments by watching its action on a small amount of water in a large bottle, occasionally shaking it to help the gas to dissolve. It became warm and light blue in colour. Priestley remembered that his friend Woulfe had noticed a similar phenomenon. But when Priestley exposed this solution to the atmosphere, it went colourless and gave off red fumes.

He then worked out an interesting demonstration of the stages in the process, bubbling the gas through a series of bottles containing a little water in each. Water in the first bottle began to sparkle, and emit gas, and then turned blue. It continued to give off gas until the colour was green; after this the colour deepened almost to black, and finally it appeared yellow By adjusting the quantities of water and the rate of flow of the red gas, he found that each stage could be shown in a separate bottle (Fig. 7). The air given off in the first two stages, he found, was nitrous air.

Numerous other experiments were carried out with this air on a number of substances, and he faithfully recorded the effects, though he was seldom able to offer any explanation. Some of these observations, such as the stages of impregnating whale oil with the red air, would provide a chemistry graduate today with a useful exercise of interpretation. A few of them, though not disputed, cannot yet be fully explained.

This work provided a number of good demonstrations for

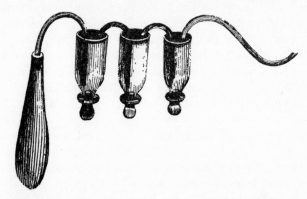

Fig. 7 Apparatus, with ground-glass joints, for showing the stages in the production of nitric acid from nitrous fumes and water.

visitors. Thus he impregnated oil of vitriol with the red air, and it appeared unchanged. He then put some in an open tumbler, added a little water, and began to stir. A cloud of dense red vapour was given off.

This experiment, when well conducted, is more remarkable than it will be expected to be found from this account of it. Several good chymists of my acquaintance have been much struck with it.

When the red air was passed into spirit of salt it turned a deep orange and gave off a peculiarly pungent odour (chlorine and nitrosyl chloride). The liquid showed all the properties of *aqua regia*, but intensified; for example, gold dissolved rapidly in the cold, and nitrous air was given off. On evaporating it to dryness he obtained a very peculiar kind of air, an acid air in which a candle was extinguished with a beautiful deep-blue flame.

Spirit of Nitre

Priestley now made a very thorough study of the preparation of spirit of nitre, using an apparatus supplied by Woulfe (Fig. 8). When oil of vitriol was distilled with nitre, the acid that came over first was the strongest, and later portions were progressively

Fig. 8 Woulfe's apparatus for the distillation of nitric acid. The distillate was collected in the bottle and surplus fumes were dissolved in water in the shallow dish.

weaker. The red fumes produced towards the end of the distillation coloured the acid, but it was nevertheless weaker than the colourless distillate. Any foreign matter in the retort, even a very small quantity, generally caused the production of brown fumes, and thus a weaker acid. This occurred with charcoal and metals, and it was therefore important to keep the materials clean and free from combustible matter (such as cork) or metal filings. Heat also coloured the purest spirit of nitre and thus weakened it.

This work on acids undoubtedly brought together much detailed information of importance in manufacturing operations.

Volatile Vitriolic Acid

Priestley still wanted to know why the two vitriolic acids, the ordinary and the volatile, were so different, and why the latter was so much weaker than the former. Arguing by analogy with the nitrous acids, he concluded that the volatile form had more phlogiston (that is, was a reduced form of the other). He also thought it should be possible to obtain inflammable air from the volatile acid, and eventually succeeded in doing this. Saturating water with vitriolic acid air over mercury, and allowing it to stand in contact with more of that air for about ten days, he then poured some of it on to zinc filings. On warming the mixture inflammable air was obtained. He also found that marine acid air was ten times as soluble in water as was vitriolic acid air, and thought that this explained why the former acted so much more readily with metals.

Pure Acids

Most of the work described above had been completed before 1777. Continuing his experiments in that year, Priestley was able to announce in his next volume (1779) his conclusion that all the mineral acids were colourless when pure.

All the books he consulted mentioned the *colour* of spirit of salt, but if the acid were made by dissolving marine acid air in water it had no colour, however strong the solution was made. He was perfectly satisfied that the colour was due to some earthy impurity, for he always made his own spirit of salt and could produce the colour at will. This, he found, was nearly always due to a small quantity of iron, which usually came from the luting materials used to seal the apparatus before distillation. Everyone who carried out experiments with iron compounds in glass vessels knew how easily the vessels became dirty and rusted, and Priestley pointed out that they could be cleaned quickly with spirit of salt, which immediately became straw-coloured, like the commercial acid.

Spirit of salt, heated in sealed glass tubes, became far more reactive than usual, even acting on the glass. When he heated a small quantity of it in this way until it had all disappeared, some 'saline matter' remained in its place. He took this out and discovered that it was a compound of lead. His friend Magellan was with him at the time. They washed the material with distilled water to remove any acid and examined it. Magellan noticed that it had the taste of sugar of lead, and the addition of cold water gave a white precipitate.

Spirit of nitre, which also he always made for himself, was likewise colourless when pure, but became coloured if any 'phlogistic' material (combustible or calcinable matter) was present or if the acid was heated. This he had shown previously, but he now found a way of demonstrating the effect of heat by enclosing a small quantity in a large sealed glass tube. This gave red fumes on heating, the colour almost disappearing on cooling. Only a small amount of the red vapour was needed to colour the acid. The vapour also reacted with other acids. With phosphoric acid, a remarkable deep indigo colour was obtained.

The reaction of the red vapour with oil of vitriol was also given attention, though Priestley was not the only chemist to carry out such work. His first striking experiment (p. 112) had been done in the autumn of 1776. He had then left some of the solution in a stoppered bottle.

But though *my* process was over, that of *nature* was not. Happening to be looking at it on the 19th of March following, perhaps about six months after the impregnation, I found . . . that almost the whole was crystallized, a very small part only of the contents of the phial remaining liquid.

On adding a little of the solid to water, air was released, and the water began to sparkle. When it was heated gently, a very large quantity of 'air' came off, and he found it to be the 'purest nitrous air'. The crystals, in fact, were a solid compound of nitrous air and oil of vitriol (nitrosyl sulphuric acid), as he showed, and the remaining liquid was spirit of nitre. All the oil of vitriol had combined with the nitrous air. Heat on the crystals made them emit dense red fumes, and after a time only oil of vitriol remained.

Another solution of the nitrous vapour in oil of vitriol was kept for about a year before it crystallized. This time the acid was not quite saturated with the vapour, but the result was worth waiting for, and he was greatly impressed with the beauty of the crystals.

Their form, as nearly as I can describe it, was that of a feather. . . . The two parts, as it were, of the feather made an angle with each other of about 160 degrees, and each of the single fibres that composed the feather, but which were connected, like the toes of a duck's foot, by the same substance . . . made an angle with the stem from which they arose of about 45 degrees. A more beautiful appearance can hardly be imagined, and I am afraid I shall never see the like again.

He continued his experiments after the manuscript had been sent to the printer, and added a section to show how the crystals could be produced as required. To do this, the acid should be concentrated and the nitrous vapour very copious. Crystals then formed readily on the sides of the bottle and not in the acid itself. The process could be speeded up by turning the bottle around so as to cover its sides with acid, filling it immediately with nitrous vapour, and setting it aside with the stopper inserted. By repeating the process, half of the acid would crystallize, the remaining liquid being spirit of nitre.

Most oil of vitriol contained a small amount of an earthy substance, but Priestley was certain this was an impurity. The acid obtained by decomposing his crystals at a boiling temperature for some time was very pure and contained no earth. Again, if instead of merely boiling off the water from oil of vitriol to concentrate it, the acid was distilled twice, all the earthy matter could be removed.

Chapter 9

What We Breathe

SOME inkling of the difficulties that surrounded the study of gases can be gained from the fact that Priestley had been actively studying the composition of the atmosphere for some eight years, from 1767 to 1775, before he had any clear ideas on the subject. Even so, his use of the term 'airs' and his wholehearted belief in Stahl's phlogiston theory make it extremely difficult to know whether he in fact understood what he had discovered as well as did some of his contemporaries. Perhaps the best way of treating this work is to do as he requested his readers to do, that is, to regard his new observations as his discoveries and his attempted explanations as opinions only—'I can only repeat, that it is not my opinions, on which I would be understood to lay any stress. Let the new facts, from which I deduce them, be considered as my discoveries, and let other persons draw better inferences from them if they can.'

Calcination of Metals

Early in their inquiries, both Priestley and Lavoisier thought that the calcination of metals would help to solve the problem of the constitution of the atmosphere. They both carried out experiments on red lead, for example, but both were confused by their results, for as yet neither had any idea as to the real difference between the part of the air that became fixed during calcination, combustion and similar processes, and Black's fixed air. Indeed, by the summer of 1774 Priestley seems to have been further from the solution of his problem than he had been two years earlier. The confusion was due in part at least to the fact that the preparation of red lead was a difficult one to carry out, and the composition of the substance was variable. It was made

9

by heating lead in air in two stages, and it contained various oxides of lead. The lower oxides, particularly after grinding, quickly take up carbon dioxide and moisture from the air, and these are liberated again on heating.

Priestley heated red lead with a candle, and obtained fixed air and a little water. All the 'air' he obtained dissolved in water and he concluded that it was pure fixed air.

Similar results were obtained by Lavoisier at about the same time, but a proportion of the air he obtained did not dissolve in water. However, Lavoisier did not test the insoluble part and did not discover what it was. Like Priestley, he concluded that in the calcination of lead the common air that had acted on the metal during its calcination had deposited the fixed air which it contained and that this was taken up by the metal.

At that time they did not know that the fixed air was absorbed by the powder *after* calcination and grinding. It is easy to underestimate the difficulty of such researches, and to forget that chemists at that time had few criteria by which to gauge the purity of the substances they worked upon. There were no lists of true chemical elements, no clear ideas as to the nature of the air, and none whatever about water. These came out of their work several years later.

These abortive calcination experiments are often used as examples of the way even the greatest experimenters were thinking about combustion problems, but they are even better examples of the difficulties they had to face and overcome. How Priestley overcame them is an important part of the discovery of oxygen.

Dephlogisticated Air (Oxygen)

Priestley obviously enjoyed telling about the way he came to make one of his greatest discoveries—dephlogisticated air. He kept his readers in suspense while he pointed some morals from his experience.

When I . . . compare my last discoveries relating to the constitution of the atmosphere with the first, I see the closest and easiest connexion in the world between them, so as to wonder that I should not have been led immediately from the one to the other. That this was not the case, I attribute to the force of prejudice, which, unknown to ourselves, biasses not only our *judgments*, properly so called, but even the perceptions of our senses: for we may take a maxim so strongly for granted, that the plainest evidence of sense will not intirely change, and often hardly modify our persuasions; and the more ingenious a man is, the more effectually he is entangled in his errors; his ingenuity only helping him to deceive himself, by evading the force of truth.

Few maxims had taken so firm a hold on the human mind as that air was a simple, elementary substance, indestructible and unalterable. All his experiments, however, had led him to believe that it was a composition of some kind. He next asked what this composition was—'what is the thing that we breathe' —and how could it be made from its constituents. He thought this could be done by heating various substances in air over mercury, suspending them or resting them on a small support inside a tube. He found he could not do this effectively with the aid of his mirror, and decided that he needed a strong burning lens.

In June 1774 he obtained a lens of 12-inch diameter and 20-inch focal length, and immediately set about 'with great alacrity to examine . . . what kind of air a great variety of substances, natural and factitious, would yield'.

It was not until 1 August, however, that he tried to obtain an air from *mercurius calcinatus per se*, that is, the substance produced when mercury is heated alone in the air. He readily obtained an 'air' that did not dissolve when water was admitted to the tube. He was extremely surprised to find also that a candle burned in this air remarkably well, much the same as it did in the air formed when iron was left in nitrous air. He knew that no nitrous material had been used in the preparation, and so he was utterly at a loss to account for it. The candle, indeed, burned with more splendour and heat than in the 'modified nitrous air'. Red-hot wood sparkled in it—like paper that had been dipped in a solution of nitre and dried—and it consumed fast.

At the same time he obtained the same air from 'the red precipitate' (the salt obtained from mercury and spirit of nitre), and in this case he thought the air was formed by the acid.

Clearly, the mercury calx had obtained something from the air that was also common to nitre. This appeared more extraordinary than it ought to have done, and he suspected the purity of the mercury calx; had he been anything of a practical chemist, he admitted, he could not have entertained any such suspicion. He therefore obtained a pure specimen of the substance from Warltire, who happened to be staying with him at Calne at the time, and from that specimen he got even more air than before.

This experiment might have satisfied any moderate sceptic: but, however, being at Paris in the October following, and knowing that there were several eminent chymists in that place, I did not omit the opportunity, by means of my friend Mr. Magellan, to get an ounce of mercurius calcinatus prepared by Mr. Cadet, of the genuineness of which there could not possibly be any suspicion; and at the same time, I frequently mentioned my surprize at the kind of air which I had got from this preparation to Mr. Lavoisier, Mr. le Roy, and several other philosophers, who honoured me with their notice in that city . . .

Right at the start, too, he had got the same air from red lead, a yellow product being left behind. Though it contained some fixed air, as he had found before, a candle burned in this specimen very strongly and with a crackling noise. He argued that, in both cases, since the calces were prepared in the same way, they must have got 'this property of being able to yield this particular kind of air' from the atmosphere itself.

As I never make the least secret of any thing that I observe, I mentioned this experiment also, as well as those with the mercurius calcinatus, and the red precipitate, to all my philosophical acquaintance at Paris, and elsewhere; having no idea, at that time, to what these remarkable facts would lead.

Immediately on his return to London in November 1774 he had got to work on Cadet's specimen, and prepared some air in which a candle burned with a vivid flame. He then submitted it to various tests to see if it resembled nitrous air. He grew more and more surprised as he found it behaved quite differently. He still thought of it as having something in common with nitrous air and nitrous acid. Now nitrous air diminished common air. Would this new air do the same? Nothing happened. The result surprised him.

He was much more surprised to find that, after the new air
had stood over water for two days, a candle still burned in it as
well as in common air. After similar treatment, the nitrous airs
he had prepared would extinguish a candle. He was therefore
forced to conclude that there was a 'very material' difference
between them and his new air.

From November of that year to the end of February 1775 he
was busy with other work, including his experiments on vitriolic
acid air (p. 108). It was at this time that he burned one of his
hands badly, and he also suffered from very painful boils, which
began in December and recurred at intervals until the following
spring; they were still troubling him when he took up his work
again at the point where he had left it.

Meanwhile he had been meditating on the problem of the
new air, and by 1 March made the decisive step; he tested it to
see if it could be diminished *with* nitrous air. This gave results;
the new air was diminished 'quite as much as common air',
and now, for the first time, he realized that it was more like
common air than nitrous air. He therefore thought that it would
be fit for breathing.

But he did not then take any notice of what in reality was the
most surprising thing of all, namely that the diminution was
greater than it would have been with common air; for he was
'so fully possessed by the notion of there being no air better
than common air'—a reasonable enough assumption. The next
day he was more surprised than ever to find that, after the
mixture of nitrous air and the new air had stood all night over
water, a candle still burned in the remaining air 'and even
better than in common air'. Despite this evidence, he thought
he had found a way of obtaining common air, and told this to
his friends, including Price. He realized that respiration tests
were necessary to complete the proof of its being common air.

It took him until 8 March to obtain a mouse, which he put
into two ounce-measures of the air, expecting it to live about a
quarter of an hour. But it lived a full half-hour, and, though it
appeared dead when he pulled it out, he was able to revive it
by holding it near the fire. This made him suspect, but still
with a little doubt, that this air was indeed better than common
air. On 9 March he tested the air the mouse had breathed,

expecting it to be noxious; but it was still better than common
air. This so puzzled him that he lay awake that night thinking
about it. In the morning he decided to add more nitrous air to
it, and, to his 'utter astonishment', he found it further reduced
to about half its volume. As he still had some of the air the
mouse had breathed, he put it in again, and it lived another
full half-hour; and this time it came out lively and vigorous.
By the next day the air had become reduced in volume from
one and a half to two-thirds of an ounce-measure, but even then
it was still almost as good as common air. He now decided to
measure the 'goodness' of this new air more accurately, and
found it four to five times as good as common air.

Turning to the question of why red lead had given a somewhat different result, he obtained the new air from it and from
massicot (fused lead monoxide), but found that it always contained a quantity of fixed air. This time he concluded that the
presence of fixed air was due to some circumstance connected
with their preparation. He therefore asked Dr Higgins to make
him some fresh red lead. This was not a good specimen, for it
had a yellowish cast and some 'pieces' were entirely yellow.
But though it contained little true red lead, the specimen did
give a little air, which this time was pure. He then tried to
convert the specimen to the form that gave much air, by adding
mineral acids, drying, pulverizing, and heating in a gun-barrel.
The specimen prepared with spirit of nitre became exceedingly
red and gave air as soon as it was heated, though this time it
was mixed with some fixed air. On moistening the red substance
with nitric acid (thus removing any carbonate) he obtained air
five times as pure as common air. He thought about a name
for the new air, and decided to call it dephlogisticated air (air
eminently suited for combustion, that is, to receive phlogiston
from combustible substances).

He now tried the effect of nitric acid on all kinds of earths,
and in every case obtained dephlogisticated air on heating. He
repeated his former experiment with saltpetre, and found that
this also gave dephlogisticated air on heating. He thought that
inflammable air might explode with more violence in this air
than in common air, but the result far exceeded his expectations; the report, he considered, was about fifty times as loud.

He then breathed the air himself, drawing it into his lungs through a syphon until he had reduced it to the standard of common air, as judged by the nitrous air test.

The feeling of it to my lungs was not sensibly different from that of common air; but I fancied that my breast felt peculiarly light and easy for some time afterwards. Who can tell but that, in time, this pure air may become a fashionable article in luxury. Hitherto only two mice and myself have had the privilege of breathing it.

This also prompted the thought that 'pure' air might be very useful in medicine, but he advocated caution, for, as a candle burns out much faster in it, so a man might 'live out too fast'.

Priestley did not stop here but went on to study the effect of spirit of nitre on many substances. He suspected that when substances burned without air, as when mixed with nitre or substances formed from the acid of nitre, that it was 'by the same property that common air itself . . . is capable of sustaining both flame and animal life'.

He had also at various times made a number of other observations about everyday processes that occurred in the atmosphere. Thus iron nails were kept in a confined volume of air from 18 December 1773 to 2 March 1775. The nails had rusted and the air was diminished by one-fifth. Thus the rusting of iron was another 'phlogistication' process. He again examined the drying of lead paints, having previously thought that the phlogistication was due to the white lead. By making up a paint with red lead and testing it in the same way (p. 79) he found that the air was phlogisticated, just as before. This effect could not have been due to the red lead and so it must have been due to the oil used, in this case turpentine. He noted, too, that it was customary to allow green matter to grow on the walls and bottoms of water reservoirs to keep the water sweet. Remembering that plants restored vitiated air, he concluded that they also took up the phlogistic matter resulting from the decay of other vegetation in the water and so helped to purify it.

Such simple observations as these were of great importance in life and Nature.

Trifling as they seem to be, they have, in a philosophical view, the greatest dignity and importance; serving to explain some of the most striking phenomena in nature, respecting the general plan and constitution of the system, and the relation that one part of it bears to another.

Respiration and the Blood

In the preface to his third volume, signed on 3 February 1777, Priestley intimated that this might be his last book on the subject of airs, as he expected to be engaged in very different pursuits in the future. He would gladly deliver the torch to any who might be disposed to carry it. His original aim had been fulfilled, and it gratified him to see 'with how much ardour and ability these pursuits are now prosecuted in very different parts of Europe'. He mentioned particularly Lavoisier and the duc de Chaulnes in France; Landriani, Fontana, Volta, and Moscati in Italy; Achard and others in Germany. Several of his friends in this country were similarly occupied, such as Falconer, Percival, Bewley, and Warltire. Magellan also, who had an extensive correspondence with continental scientists and had himself instructed many of them in the best way of carrying out experiments with airs, told him that many more people than these were actively following his work. Priestley hoped that through their efforts many of the problems he had left unsolved would be dealt with, and that many other of nature's secrets would soon be unfolded. On taking leave of the subject (as he thought), he explained why he considered that the new types of experiments he had introduced would prove of value to the progress of natural knowledge.

The reason of my great expectations from this mode of experimenting is simply this, that, by exhibiting substances *in the form of air*, we have an opportunity of examining them in a less compounded state, and are advanced one step nearer to their primitive elements.

The most important memoir in this volume was a paper that had been read to the Royal Society on 25 January 1776, and was now reprinted to give it a wider distribution. It represented the beginnings of a scientific account of respiration. Despite the importance of respiration in physiology, no one had yet found out its real function; it might, indeed, have continued to elude direct investigation, as Priestley said, had it not 'discovered itself' in the course of his researches. Respiration, in the language of Priestley, was a phlogistic process; it diminished air in a certain proportion, lessened its specific gravity, and made it unfit to support life or flame. In terms of the phlogiston theory, the blood was specially suited to take up phlogiston and to release it, the colour of the blood changing in the process. His early ideas on the subject (p. 74) were no longer tenable.

He first recorded the experiments of others to show that the florid colour of the blood was due to contact with air. Father Beccaria, one of Priestley's correspondents, had done some work at Cigna's request; he put blood in a vacuum, and found that it always remained blackish, but reverted to red on exposure to air. Priestley inferred from this that 'the air we breathe may be so far decomposed, as to communicate something of nitre to the blood, in its passage through the lungs'. Judging by his remarks elsewhere, he seems to have meant by 'something of nitre' that property possessed in common by the air and by nitre. Though his explanation on the point is not clear, he went on to show that he was thinking of dephlogisticated air in this connection, for he demonstrated his point by taking sheep's blood and allowing the serum to separate, and then supporting the blackest parts of the blood in gauze nets over water and over mercury, and examining the effects of various airs on the congealed masses. They went red in common air, and especially in dephlogisticated air; and they became black again in any air that was unfit for respiration. When placed alternately in phlogisticated and dephlogisticated air, the congealed blood changed readily from red to black and back again.

To be absolutely sure that it was the air acting through the serum that produced the red colour, he put two lots of congealed blood in similar cups, covered them with serum, and left one in air and the other in a vacuum. The first went red and the other black. The red one again went black when put into phlogisticated air or left in a hermetically sealed vessel.

Further Applications

As a result mainly of his discovery of dephlogisticated air and its far-reaching consequences, Priestley found that he was unable to give up his scientific researches; indeed, this work had led him into wider fields of science, and within two years he had materials for a new volume. The change of emphasis is clear from the full title of the work: *Experiments and Observations relating to various branches of Natural Philosophy; with a continuation of the observations on Air.* It was published in 1779 and dedicated to Savile. In this, as in some other recent works, he reiterated his strong plea for the introduction of natural science into the school syllabus.

Four years before this, Priestley had formed the opinion that dephlogisticated air was a compound of nitric acid and an earth. The opinion seems to have been based partly on the fact that when nitric acid was added to any earth, and the product heated, dephlogisticated air was obtained. This seemed to be consistent with his work on the fluor acid air, which, in the presence of water, did in fact yield a strong acid and a genuine gritty earth. But some of his latest experiments made him doubt whether there was any acid at all in pure air. He had now obtained pure air from spirit of nitre and salts made from it; from alum, green vitriol and some other salts of vitriolic acid; and from some minerals, such as manganese (dioxide) which seemed never to have been in contact with the atmosphere.

The results he obtained with the vitriols had been questioned, and he went to considerable trouble to verify them. On 24 November 1777, by heating green vitriol (ferrous sulphate) at a dull red heat, he obtained water vapour, a little fixed air, a large quantity of vitriolic acid air, and a residuum that was diminished by nitrous air; a purplish ochre was left behind. Suspecting that there might have been some nitre present, he made his own green vitriol, but obtained the same results. He now suspected the purity of the vitriolic acid he was using, and so repeated it with some acid that had been prepared without spirit of nitre. He obtained the same result, except that there was very little fixed air in the product. He now repeated the experiment so that none of the materials came into contact with the external air. Some of his chemist friends still maintained that all oil of vitriol contained some spirit of nitre, and so he obtained from Winch a fresh specimen of his own making guaranteed to contain no spirit of nitre. He still obtained dephlogisticated air. He put more vitriolic acid on the ochre left at the end of the experiment, evaporated it, and heated as before; he obtained more dephlogisticated air. He now did the same with blue and white vitriol, with similar results, and confirmed Landriani's report that pure air could be obtained by heating the salt produced from mercury and vitriolic acid.

Being perfectly satisfied that the salts of these two acids yielded pure air on heating, he turned to the salts of spirit of salt. No pure air was obtained from corrosive sublimate (mercuric chloride), from common salt, or from the salt obtained by dissolving iron in spirit of salt.

Upon the whole, I think I may conclude . . . that the marine acid differs essentially from both the vitriolic and nitrous in this, that it cannot, by any combination whatever, be made to yield dephlogisticated air, at least with the degree of heat that I was able to apply.

This was one of the experimental rocks on which Lavoisier's theory (that all acids contain oxygen) was to founder, and may well have been one of the reasons why Priestley could not accept the name 'oxygen', as the acidifying principle. He did not, however, make use of such an argument explicitly, perhaps because there was no proof that pure air could not be obtained from the marine acid in some other way than the one he had tried.

Combining Volumes

By now it is clear that Priestley's chemical writings were of value to his contemporaries chiefly for the large number of new facts they contained and for the frequent hints he gave as to what lines of research might lead to further discoveries. In the introduction to his fourth volume, he outlined some of his main results, one of which, dealing with the proportions in which nitrous air and dephlogisticated air combine, shows that he had been giving some attention to this question. He gave it as his belief that 'the purest dephlogisticated air will not . . . require more than two equal measures of nitrous air'. Some years earlier, when studying the actions in which inflammable air is obtained from marine acid air, he noted that the volume of the former was one-half that of the latter.

He now gave the results of his attempt to measure the exact proportion in which nitrous air and dephlogisticated air combined. At first he found that two measures of the former and one of the latter were reduced, after reacting and shaking with water, to one-half of a measure. If they were 'peculiarly pure', they were reduced to only one-sixth of a measure. Trying the experiment one day in a different way, he found that two measures of the former and one of the latter were reduced to three-hundredths of a measure, or a little less. On repeating the experiment, he found that two measures of the former were rather more than enough to 'saturate' one of the latter. Not willing to go beyond the observed facts, he said that 'it cannot be supposed, that *exactly* two measures of nitrous air should be the precise quantity that would produce the greatest diminution'. If it could not be supposed, that is, accepted without proof, that the combining proportions had a simple ratio to one another, this statement was, to say the least, a very suggestive one. His next was more so.

I am inclined to think that, were it possible to make both the nitrous and dephlogisticated air in the greatest purity, and then to mix them in some exact proportion, the aerial form of them both would be entirely destroyed, the whole quantity seeming to disappear, as in the mixture of alkaline and acid air.

The latter gave a solid product, whereas the product of the former dissolved in the water over which they were mixed.

Plants in Sunlight

In 1771 and 1772 Priestley had discovered that vitiated air could be restored by sprigs of mint (p. 73). Scheele, on the other hand, had shown that germinating seeds produced the converse effect. Both were correct, and Priestley decided that the subject deserved further examination. He repeated his earlier experiments in 1777 and gave close attention to the matter in the spring and summer of 1778. At the time, he was not aware that anyone else was doing similar work.

In repeating his experiments with 'injured' air, he found a greater variety in the effects produced than he had noticed before. Some plants made the air worse. With growing plants, such as strawberry shoots whose roots were still in the earth, the air was improved. He also had some examples of *common air* being improved, successful results being obtained in June 1778 with strawberry shoots, winter savoury, and parsley.

From this he concluded that the action of a plant on the air when vegetating was quite different from that of the 'exhalation of the flower, and perhaps of other parts'. In July, when he was on the coast, he wondered whether the air enclosed in the bladders of seaweed would help to confirm his views. From bladders that appeared to be in a state of healthy growth he obtained air that was better than common air, but from those that had blackened the air was much worse.

In the course of the experiments at Calne he had noticed bubbles coming from the stalks and roots of several plants. To find what these were, he put about ten sprigs of mint into a jar of water and in a week had collected one half ounce-measure of the air. On 19 June 1778 he tested it and found it 'very pure' (oxygen). But his satisfaction was short-lived. On removing the plants from the jar, air continued to be produced just as well in their absence! He also saw that 'air' was being produced in another vessel standing in a window where the sun was shining. He quickly noticed that both vessels had a 'green kind of matter' partly covering them on the inside. The growth of green and brown algae on the jars must have been a common occurrence in the past, but he had thought nothing about it.

He took the vessel from the window, filled it with pump water, and put it back. Bubbles began to rise so fast that in three days he had seven ounce-measures of 'very pure' air. Many of his vessels now had this green matter, so he did the same with them all, and soon collected a considerable quantity of dephlogisticated air, especially when the jars were placed in the sun.

Having to leave Calne on a journey which occupied some months, he arranged a few experiments so that he could continue with the inquiry as soon as he returned. Clean jars were set up in troughs containing rain-water, river water, and pump water. When he next examined them, the first two had produced nothing; but green matter had appeared in the one with pump water, which he knew contained a considerable quantity of fixed air. He then placed some large jars containing rain-water, river water, pump water, and pump water impregnated with fixed air in his garden. It was now autumn, and when he examined the jars on 14 October, there was green matter in the jar containing impregnated pump water, but not in the others.

He found also that the green matter was produced in the absence of air, and so concluded at first that it was neither animal nor vegetable. He examined it with a microscope, and saw that it consisted of a few hollow filaments and 'some globular pieces, perforated with some regularity'. His botanist friends, however, were convinced that it was a plant.

He also noticed that light appeared to be necessary for the green matter to be produced.

I have had some appearances, which, extraordinary as it will seem, make it rather probable, that *light* is necessary to the formation of this substance; but many more observations, which I believe can only be made in the summer season, will be necessary to determine this.

He was fairly certain about it, however; for the green matter was not produced in the dark, and heat in the absence of light likewise produced nothing. If there was fixed air in the water, the green matter caused it all to disappear, the air present being nothing but pure dephlogisticated air.

For no fixed air at all, but only the purest dephlogisticated air, is at length procured from it; and water impregnated with fixed air yields, after this exposure, the greatest quantity of dephlogisticated air.

Being curious about other waters, he took two specimens from Bristol Hot-well, leaving one in the sun and keeping the other dark. Air extracted from the former was much better than that from the latter. His friend Percival also examined air extracted from sea-water, and found that this was better than common air. This interesting fact made him ask his readers to repeat the experiment with other samples of water.

Priestley's fifth volume, though not published until he had moved to Birmingham, contained his last work at Calne, and gave a few more particulars about the green matter. As a result of examinations by some of his friends, there was no longer any doubt about its being a plant. He tells us that his own eyes had always been weak, and so he relied on the descriptions of others as much as possible. He concluded that the seeds of this plant must float invisibly in the air and be present in the water used for the green matter to be produced. Thus none will ever grow in distilled water placed over mercury and left in the sun.

That light was of importance to plants was obvious from the fact that if allowed to grow in the dark they became white and sickly. Thus he thought it inadvisable for plants to be kept in a bedroom at night, since the air would be vitiated. Provided they received enough light, plants could grow in the air or in water. Thus he collected half a dozen different kinds of pond plants and found that they all gave dephlogisticated air when placed under water in inverted jars standing in the sun.

This led him to begin some experiments to find whether the dephlogisticated air was produced by light and something within the plant, but they were inconclusive.

What further interesting work he might have done was prevented by his learning that Ingenhousz had already investigated the problem. However, before leaving the subject, and finding that the natural history of what he called the 'green vegetable substance' was unknown, he added what he had observed about its growth. This he did in part to counteract Ingenhousz's ideas on its origin, namely that 'the water itself, or some substance in the water, is . . . changed into this vegetation, and undergoes . . . such a metamorphosis, as to become what we now call dephlogisticated air'. Priestley thought this to be a rather extraordinary idea, 'considering how long the doctrine of *equivocal*, or *spontaneous generation*, has been exploded'. Ingenhousz thought it was no more surprising than, say, the change of grass to fat in the body of a ruminant, but Priestley justly pointed out that 'the change of *water*, into an *organized plant*, is a thing of a very different nature'.

He stated that the 'seeds' of this plant, 'for I presume that, like other plants, this also must have seeds', float invisibly in the air and grow into plants whenever they meet with water. Being so minute, they insinuate themselves through the smallest apertures, and grow quickly in a few days, particularly if the water is impregnated with not too much vegetable or animal matter in a state of putrefaction, which seemed to be the richest food (or *pabulum*) for the plant.

While Priestley had been working with whole plants, Ingenhousz had carried out experiments with leaves, and found that the production of dephlogisticated air in sunlight took place at the leaves and especially on their under sides. These results were published in 1779, before Priestley's work was available in print, although it was known to several of his friends. For some years Ingenhousz thought it unjust that Priestley should claim to have discovered the importance of light in this connection, and in 1787 Priestley attempted to place the matter in its correct perspective. He outlined the course of his earlier work and said that what Ingenhousz had done with leaves was entirely independent of his own work on complete plants, 'but the same summer, and the same sun operated for us both, and you certainly published before me'.

Another aspect of this question—whether fixed air could be regarded as a food of plants—was of particular interest to Thomas Percival in Manchester. More than a hundred experiments were carried out in 1775 and afterwards by Percival and his friends, and the results were always the same when the gas was applied to the leaves—'that fixed air, in a due proportion, is so favourable to vegetable growth, that it may justly be deemed a pabulum of plants'. Some of Priestley's experiments with algae had also confirmed this, but he refused to accept the evidence. Whenever a plant was put into pure fixed air it died, and so it could not be regarded as wholesome for plants. He wrote to Percival:

In all these cases, you will say, I choak the plants with too great a quantity of *wholesome* nourishment. And to all yours I say, you do not give them enough of the *noxious matter* to kill them.

He was eventually convinced, not by the work of his Manchester friends, but by the experiments of Senebier in Geneva, of which he heard in 1784. These appeared to show that plants effected a conversion of fixed air into dephlogisticated air.

Chapter 10

Sunshine at Fair Hill

THE period that was to prove the happiest in Priestley's life—
the eleven years after he left Shelburne—began inauspiciously.
Throughout the summer of 1780 he endured a long and painful
illness, apparently the first of several occasions when he suffered
from gallstones. By the terms of the agreement, his income on
leaving his patron was reduced from about £300, if the
allowance for experiments is taken into account, to £150. Thus
at first he thought it would be necessary to take in pupils to
cover the expense of educating his three sons and a daughter.
Some eight years before, Priestley had made it clear that he
disliked the idea of being entirely dependent upon one patron,
and that he would prefer small grants from wealthy individuals
who were as interested in promoting religious and civil liberty
as they were in helping the advancement of science. In the
event, his future work was supported in this way.

Among the friends who early saw that Priestley's discoveries
would be of importance to medicine was the Quaker physician,
John Fothergill, who remained sympathetic towards his views
on most questions. It was for the physician, Fothergill wrote,
'to take up the various substances in nature where the philosopher leaves them, and to avail himself of their particular
properties for the preservation of health or for the cure of
diseases'. Apart from his interest in remedies based on fixed air,
both as gas and in solution, Fothergill had been the first to see
the possibilities of using oxygen in 'restoring animation'. He
was quick to form clear ideas as to why oxygen was necessary
to life, and suggested that the union of oxygen with phlogistic
matter in the body was the cause of animal heat.[1]

In about 1777 Fothergill, sensing that financial considerations

[1] W. Hawes, *Transactions of the Royal Humane Society from 1774 to 1784*, n.d., 278.

might be deterring Priestley from following up some of his discoveries to their logical conclusions, offered to raise for him a further £100 a year. Priestley had declined the offer, thinking that Shelburne might take offence, but he agreed to accept a smaller sum, £40, contributed by three Yorkshiremen— Fothergill, Savile, and William Constable—together with Sir Theodore Jansen, formerly Lord Mayor of London. When Fothergill heard that Priestley was leaving Lord Shelburne, he forthwith arranged to extend this support. Soon afterwards Priestley could name fourteen regular subscribers, most of whom were equally interested in his religious work. Many others came forward to assist him. Mrs Rayner, whom he had met through the Essex Street chapel, gave him £100 to cover the cost of moving, and followed this with another gift of £400. William Heberden, an eminent London physician who also attended services at Essex Street, came next to her in generosity. Lee and others continued to help him from time to time. Though Priestley never lacked enemies, these facts are a remarkable testimony to his great capacity for friendship and to the value placed upon his work by people of varied interests and outlook.

But this was not all. His brothers-in-law, John and William Wilkinson, now prosperous ironmasters, came forward as generous kinsmen. As soon as the Priestleys had decided to settle in the Midlands, John Wilkinson found them a house on the outskirts of Birmingham at Fair Hill, near the Sparkbrook turnpike gate, to which they moved in September 1780. The house, and the surrounding land, was owned by Sampson Lloyd, the most active partner in the banking house of Taylor and Lloyd (founded 1765), now Lloyds Bank. The original partners, Sampson Lloyd senior and John Taylor, were representatives of the newly emerging class of wealthy industrialists, Lloyd being a merchant and ironmaster, and Taylor a remarkably successful japanner and toy-maker.[1]

Both house and grounds were ample for a family of the middle class. On the ground floor there were a drawing-room for the entertainment of visitors, front and back parlours fitted with Bath stoves, kitchen and store-room, and back kitchen equipped with coppers. A wide staircase led to the four main bedrooms

[1] S. Lloyd, *The Lloyds of Birmingham*, Birmingham, 1907, 51 ff.

above, and, in addition, there was a hall and back staircase leading to the attic floor, half of which became one long room to house Priestley's library and some instruments, the rest being used as living accommodation for two maids and a servant boy. Outside was the brewhouse, with a laundry above, together with a pigsty, sheds for coal and coke (of which a normal supply was about twenty tons), and a 'garden tool house', well enough stocked to enable him to maintain plots for growing vegetables, and neat lawns, which he tended carefully with roller and scythe. Only one thing seemed lacking—a suitable building for use as a laboratory—and this gave him the opportunity to design one exactly according to his special requirements. On 30 November 1780 he reported to Wedgwood that his health was good again, except that he found it necessary to keep to a vegetable diet, that his laboratory was built, and that everything was nearly ready 'to do more business in a philosophical way than ever'.

By this time he had lost two of his earlier intimate friends. Fothergill, to whom he owed the subscription that ensured his independence and ability to continue his scientific studies, had died; his place was taken up immediately by Samuel Galton and his son, who were to become great friends of the Priestleys, though as yet they were strangers. And now Wedgwood informed him that Bentley, one of the first to encourage him at Warrington, had also died. In his reply, Priestley said that in a few days he would have written to Bentley to tell him about his new home and that another volume of experiments was due to go to the printer in about a month.

Few of my friends interested themselves as much as he did in the success of my philosophical pursuits, and I shall now feel . . . less interested in them myself. For the pleasure of communicating our discoveries is one great means of engaging us to enter upon and pursue such laborious investigations . . .
No person wished more ardently than Mr. Bentley, that I should have the leisure I now have the prospect of enjoying, for the study of Nature.

Though Wedgwood's name appeared in the list of Priestley's subscribers, there were others who, for feelings of delicacy, set out to help him anonymously on his arrival in the Midlands.

Among these were Dr Erasmus Darwin (whose son, Robert, married Wedgwood's daughter, Susan, and became the father of Charles Darwin), and Matthew Boulton, owner of the great Soho Works in Birmingham that became known as 'Europa's wonder and Britannia's pride' (Plate 13). James Watt had joined Boulton in 1774, when there was but little interest in his steam-engines, but by 1781 it could be said that 'people in London, Manchester and Birmingham are steam-mill mad'. On 10 March 1781 Wedgwood told Boulton of Darwin's reaction to the idea of giving additional support to Priestley.[1]

Our good friend, Dr. Darwin, agrees with us in the sentiment, that it would be a pity that Dr. Priestley should have any cares or cramps to interrupt him in the fine vein of experiments he is in the midst of, and is willing to devote his time to the pursuit of, for the public good. The Doctor will subscribe, and has thought of some friends who he is convinced will gladly do the same. You will see from the enclosed list that one cannot decently exceed ten guineas unless it be under cover of a friends name, which method I shall take if I think it necessary; but that is the subscription I shall begin with and for three years certain. Dr. Darwin will be very cautious who he mentions this affair to, for reasons of delicacy which will have equal weight with us all. I mentioned your generous intention to Dr. P., and that we thought of £20 each; but that you will perceive cannot be, and the Doctor says much less will suffice, as he can go on very well with £100 per annum.

In his reply, Boulton expressed the hope that Wedgwood would 'manage the affair so that we may contribute our mites to so laudable a plan without the Doctor knowing anything of the matter'.

Though some were prevented in this way from being as generous as they would have liked, yet they found other means of helping, by making presents of apparatus, instruments, and books. In due course Priestley had not only a number of complete sets of Wedgwood tableware, and many special items of earthenware for the laboratory, but also metal goods and ornamental pieces from Boulton and the Wilkinsons; and all glass instruments required in the laboratory were supplied by

[1] Reproduced in Julia Wedgwood (C. H. Herford, ed.), *The Personal Life of Josiah Wedgwood the Potter*, London, 1915.

Parker of Fleet Street, who manufactured machines for preparing artificial mineral waters, the sale of which ran into
thousands, both for home use and export. Almost everything
Priestley possessed represented the best produce of British skill
and industry at that time.

Occasionally Priestley, to whom useful employment was of
far greater importance than physical comfort or riches, was
somewhat embarrassed by offers of help. On two occasions he
declined government pensions, preferring not to be beholden to
any administration or to lose independence even to the slightest
degree. In the main, the subscription method served him well.
Once, in 1785, he happened to mention to his old friend,
Thomas Percival, that a few subscribers had fallen off without
giving any reason, but the result of this admission surprised and
even appeared to vex him.[1] In 1781 Percival had been one of
the founders of the Literary and Philosophical Society at
Manchester, and Priestley had been elected an honorary
member soon afterwards. On hearing of Priestley's dilemma,
Percival wrote to a circle of his friends:

Could we not, by small annual contributions, raise a fund for the
support of this excellent philosopher's pursuits? Two guineas per
annum from twenty persons would, I think, suffice. Be so good as
to consider this proposal, and to inform me what number you think
might accede to it . . .

Such an expression of goodwill would have pleased Priestley,
particularly as so small an amount from any one person was
involved. But Percival changed his plan, thinking that the gift
would come better from the Literary and Philosophical Society.
When the suggestion was considered, the Society passed two
resolutions 'with the most cordial unanimity', as follows:

(1) The Literary and Philosophical Society of Manchester, taking
into mature consideration the importance of those experiments and
researches in which the Rev. Dr. Priestley is engaged, to the interest
of the arts, of commerce, and of science; and desirous to offer a
tribute of respect to so distinguished a member of their institution,
unanimously resolve, that a sum not less than 50 L. shall be remitted

[1] T. Percival, *Works*, London, 1807, i, p. c.

to him by their authority, and in their name, for the purpose of promoting and extending his philosophical pursuits.

(2) Resolved, that the subscription so liberally formed by several members of this Society, for the purpose of carrying into effect the contribution above proposed, be received as a part of the fund of the Society appropriated to the use which has been specified; and that the deficiency of it be supplied, if necessary, out of the joint stock now in the treasurer's hands.

Percival, reporting this to a friend in Chester, said that 'no deficiency occurred, the subscription was instantly completed with a degree of zeal and generosity which reflects great honour on the members of our Institution'.

At that time, though his situation changed later, Priestley was able to tell Percival:

I am as rich as I wish to be. My sons will have employments, which I prefer to estates, under their uncles; so that I really think my lot the happiest in the world, as I can devote my whole time to useful and pleasing pursuits; and if one fail, I can fly to another.

For several years Priestley was happy at Birmingham in his home and family circle, in his social connections, and in his religious, philosophical, and scientific activities. Not far away lived William Russell, a metal merchant and one of Birmingham's more prominent citizens. With him and his family the Priestleys became intimate. The Russells kept excellent stables that were at all times available for Priestley's service, and this saved him the trouble of looking after a horse. Other close friends were also 'merchants', such as the Rylands (wire-drawers and pin-makers) and the Galtons (gun-makers).

The children of such families were among the frequent visitors to Fair Hill, and one of them, John Ryland, left a short description of the things that most impressed his young mind. First, in front of the house, stood the Doctor's rain-gauge. Then he was allowed to run around with the 'perambulator'—a wheel provided with a handle and a device for recording distances in yards and miles—a simple instrument but a robust one to which the children became very attached. A favourite with the boys was the air-gun, a second-hand one obtained for Priestley by Adam Walker, a popular lecturer on science, soon after they came to Birmingham. Priestley usually produced it when asked,

and would often load it for them, occasionally taking his turn
at firing, 'which he pleasantly did, though he seemed very much
occupied in his laboratory, which was close at hand'. John
went on to say: 'The mark which we most delighted in was the
block upon which the Doctor's wig was dressed, which we
placed on the wall of the coal-hole to shoot at.'

Normally the laboratory was open and the children could go
in and out as they pleased when their father was present. 'I was
very much struck as a child, seeing the Doctor wear a short
apron when employed about his laboratory. Sometimes I saw
him bring his shovel to the parlour fire-place to take fire to his
laboratory, as he would not suffer any other person to enter it
for that purpose.' But not only were his fires and new furnaces
a possible danger to the children. Mischievous fingers could
wreck his experiments, as so many of the gases he worked on
were kept in bottles that appeared to be empty or to have more
or less water in them. Specimens of air were sent from various
parts of the country for analysis, and some of his correspondents,
such as Arthur Young, were pleased to take advantage of his
advice on air and water collected in connection with agri-
cultural problems.

The children also remembered being taken upstairs to the
library—a long room with books all round on shelves reaching
from the floor to the ceiling—the roll-up screen for magic
lantern shows, and the thrill of shocks from the electrical
machine kept there. These interludes pleased Priestley, who was
not easily ruffled and who enjoyed the company of the young.
John said: 'I never recollect seeing the Doctor angry but on
one occasion. He was very much mortified in consequence of a
playmate of his children uncorking a bottle containing a
peculiar kind of air which he had been a long time collecting
for one of his important experiments. In consequence of this
the laboratory was shut up against us for some time.' And
Mrs Priestley's tact was put to the test on another difficult
occasion when their much-loved daughter, Sally, decided to
clean the laboratory for her father, who had been away from
home for a period. With great care she washed out all the
bottles for him.

London was not the only centre of organized scientific

activities at that time. During the eighteenth century groups of men with common interests, varying from art and letters to agriculture and manufacturing industry, formed societies in which the pursuit of science played a prominent part, as at Liverpool, Newcastle, and Manchester. In the 1780s, one of the most important of these from the scientific and industrial points of view was the semi-formal Lunar Society, centred on Birmingham. There has always been an atmosphere of romance about this society, which met on an afternoon near the full moon at the house of one or other of the members, to dine and discuss current scientific questions, afterwards taking advantage of the moonlight to obtain some protection from such hazards of the roads as ruts and robbers.

These were parties for men only, the womenfolk and the servants being kept fully employed in seeing to their entertainment. This group of vivacious and enthusiastic men, with their convivial meetings and strange experiments, did not meet with universal respect. 'Our butler called them the Lunatics,' said Mary Anne Galton. But she did remember how impressive they were. There was Boulton, 'the father of Birmingham'; his partner, Watt, whose 'immense general knowledge was the delight of all who knew him'; Captain James Keir, 'the wit, the man of the world, the finished gentleman', who gave animation to the party; Priestley, whose serenity never failed to impress—'a man of admirable simplicity, gentleness, and kindness of heart, united with great acuteness of intellect'; together with certain medical men and botanists—Dr Stoke, 'profoundly scientific and eminently absent'; Dr Darwin, of ponderous frame but lively intellect, a scholar and poet; and Dr William Withering, who became well known for his work on the foxglove (digitalis) and its use in medicine, of whom it was said, as his life was ending in a slow decline: 'the Flower of Physic is indeed Withering'.

These men and their friends, such as Galton, Wilkinson, Wedgwood, Edgeworth, and Samuel Parr, and visitors from other parts, such as Banks and Solander, ensured that the meetings would be memorable indeed, and it was this society, more than any other, that Priestley was to miss so greatly in later years.

Here politics and religion were not allowed to intrude. Whigs and Tories, atheists, Anglicans, and Unitarians joined in the common study of nature. Even in this restricted field there were differences enough, but they learned to respect other men's points of view and endeavoured to reconcile them. By extending the common ground among the peoples of the world, in art, science, medicine, and commerce, Priestley saw great hope for the eventual realization of the brotherhood of man and universal peace. But with America struggling for independence, and with most of the countries of Europe yearning for liberty, he was aware that such dreams belonged to the distant future. He could scarcely overlook the fact that part of his security depended on the success of John Wilkinson, who could now bore cannon more accurately than any other ironmaster, so that his name had spread throughout Europe. But Wilkinson also had the foresight to adapt his machine to the boring of cylinders for steam-engines, and he enjoyed the monopoly for the Boulton & Watt engines for more than two decades. To some extent Priestley shared these interests, and on at least one occasion rode on horseback with Boulton to Colebrookdale, where the smoke from the extensive ironworks rose to form a blue haze that was visible from such vantage points as the Beacon near the Galtons' home at Great Barr.

Priestley had visited the Soho Works during his early days in Shelburne's service, and it was from there (as also from John Whitehurst of Derby, who made him the weights for his balance) that he obtained his supplies of Derbyshire spar (p. 110). Afterwards, in November 1775, Priestley had written to Boulton:

It will be a great pleasure to me to see your improvements in *fire engines*, and all your other valuable improvements in *mechanics*, and the *arts*, whenever I may have an opportunity of seeing Birmingham . . .

I shall not quarrel with you on account of our different sentiments in Politics — When I tell you what is fact, that the Americans have constructed a canon on a new principle, by which they can hit a mark at the distance of a mile, you will say their *ingenuity* has come in aid of their *cowardice*. I would tell you the principle of it, but that I am afraid you would set your superior ingenuity at work to improve upon it, for the use of their enemies.

Not long after this, he had enlisted Boulton's help in his inquiries into the state of air in factories.

I wish to procure air as it is actually breathed by the different manufacturers in this kingdom and hope you will be so obliging as to procure me the proper samples from Birmingham . . . in those places where you suspect the air to be the worst, on account of bad fumes, or a number of people working together . . . I should be glad also to have the air of some of your closest streets, and likewise the best in your neighbourhood, noting the state of the weather at the time.

Priestley's interest in the air of factories and mines continued after his arrival in Birmingham, and there is no doubt that he tried to make the industrial autocrats of his circle conscious of their responsibilities in such matters, though always with extreme tact. Thus in 1785 he told Boulton that a Dissenter of his acquaintance, a man of whom he held a high opinion, had been suffering greatly through his employment as a 'chaper', presumably one of those engaged in making buckles of the more expensive kind in imitation of jewellery—one of Boulton's early specialities. The man's eyes were affected, and he needed a change of work. Priestley left this to Boulton's conscience, saying that he was confident that Boulton would always be ready to do the right, and even generous, thing.

Just as Priestley had been on good terms with Cavendish in London, and had profited from his practical ability, wide knowledge, and general hints, so now he turned to James Watt as a friend with whom he could talk over his problems, being assured of a sympathetic hearing. Priestley admired Watt's inventiveness, and, apart from the steam-engine, he was interested in Watt's copying machines, one of which he kept in his library. Watt invented his process, later known as press-copying, as a means of avoiding excessive labour in taking copies of documents and drawings during his frequent excursions to Cornwall and elsewhere on the firm's behalf. In an attempt to reduce this drudgery, he tried writing with ink mixed with gum arabic or sugar, and found that on pressing it against a damp sheet of unsized tissue paper a reversed copy was obtained that could be read by looking through the sheet. He also designed a roller-press for taking off the impressions. The process was patented in 1780, and it played an important part in the business world until it and similar processes were replaced by the typewriter and carbon copies. Many merchants were interested, and 150 machines were sold in the first year. After this there was a steady sale throughout the period of the patent.

James Keir was well known in the Midlands as a man of science with industrial connections. After completing his medical studies at Edinburgh, where he met Erasmus Darwin, he went into the Army during the war with France, saw active service in the West Indies, and was then stationed for a time in Ireland. By about 1775 he was established as a glass manufacturer at Stourbridge, and in 1776 a study he made of the crystallization of glass was communicated to the Royal Society by George Fordyce. He had also translated Macquer's *Dictionnaire de Chymie*, a very useful book in its day.

Through Darwin, Keir became acquainted with Boulton and Watt, and in 1778 he gave up his glass factory with the object of becoming a partner at Soho. For financial reasons this did not materialize, and, apart from a short period when he looked after the works, he appears to have been concerned mainly with the letter-copying machine business. In 1779, however, he took out a patent for an alloy (about 55 % copper, 40 % zinc, and 5 % iron) of a golden colour that closely resembled Muntz's metal of 1832. This was made and marketed by Boulton, and was used for a time for making window casements, some of which were supplied to Windsor Castle, Carlton House, and other mansions. Keir then became a partner of Alexander Blair, a brother officer from the Army, and began to manufacture alkali, soap, and other materials at Tipton. Later they again joined forces to manage the Tividale Colliery in Staffordshire.

Keir had followed closely the work of the British pneumatic chemists, and particularly the recent developments at the hands of Priestley, and in 1777 he produced a *Treatise on the Various Kinds of permanently elastic Fluids, or Gases*, as an appendix to his second English edition of Macquer's *Dictionnaire*—to take the place of the article on 'fixable air'. Priestley, like Boyle, Hales, Black, Cavendish, and others, had used the term 'air'. Keir objected that chemists meant something quite different from air when they spoke of the various elastic fluids, and that general terms like fixable, fixed, or factitious air no longer enabled them to speak clearly on these topics. The language of the chemists, he said, was now at variance with the popular language, and while that state of affairs continued the progress of science would be obstructed. The word gas (plural gases) should be used, he maintained, as it was already familiar through the works of van Helmont, and there was no need to invent another term. The suggestion was simple and practical, but Priestley merely smiled at this proposed abandonment of a British tradition. However, he was probably right in thinking that Keir had read too much into van Helmont's ideas.

While at Calne, Priestley had learnt that Keir was acquainted with Boulton, and so used this channel to pass on his objections. He also criticized an experiment Keir had described, which contradicted some of Priestley's conclusions.

Whether it be owing to the persons being unaccustomed to these experiments, or some other cause, I find very few who make them with due circumspection. I consider Mr Keir as a very able chymist, and useful writer; but I cannot help smiling at his new phraseology and his puffing of *Van Helmont*.

Priestley has often been criticized for this attitude to new ways of thinking and new terminology, and it has even been said that he lacked a historical sense. But it was rather his attachment to history, and his reluctance to depart from traditions that had served mankind well, that made him stick to the old so long as the new failed to meet all objections that could be raised against it. Thus he clung to 'air' and to phlogiston long after these terms and the associated ideas had ceased to promote the progress of science.

Despite this difference of opinion, Keir and Priestley became and remained friendly throughout the period of the latter's stay at Birmingham. Keir was an Anglican, but they both welcomed the opening phases of the French Revolution and had similar political ideals.

William Withering was the last, and probably the most distinguished, of the well-known scientists and men of industry whom Priestley afterwards named as his chief friends within the Lunar Society. Though he opposed Priestley's phlogistic ideas, relations between them appear to have been consistently good. They had corresponded before Priestley came to Birmingham, as Withering was especially interested in botany and in the way Priestley's experiments illustrated the part played by plants in the renovation of the atmosphere. He was also eager to promote the use of artificial mineral waters and had devised a machine in which the gas generator could be detached from the vessel holding the 'aerated' water, so that the latter could be enclosed in an elegant mahogany container and kept on the sideboard for use as required, the only visible part of the apparatus being a simple tap. This was described in the volume of experiments Priestley published shortly after his arrival at Fair Hill.

Withering lived in the Square, with a house for medical consultations in Temple Row; from 1785 Edgbaston Hall was his country residence. He had already published the first edition of his *Arrangement of British Plants* in 1776, and this continued to be one of his major interests until the third edition of 1796. He produced translations of Bergman's books on mineralogy and the analysis of mineral waters, and some of his papers on chemical and mineral analysis were published by the Royal Society. Priestley took a lively interest in this work. Withering had made a special study of what are now called barium compounds, of special importance for Wedgwood's 'jasper ware', and Werner later named the mineral witherite (barium carbonate) after him.

Withering owned family property in Staffordshire, including three mills at Moddershall, which were used by Wedgwood for grinding some of his raw materials. As Priestley and Withering were within easy reach of each other, it is not surprising that only a few letters have survived. From these it is clear that Priestley gained much impetus in his work from contact with these men of very considerable attainments. 'One of the things that I regret the most on being expelled from Birmingham,' he wrote to Withering in 1792, 'is the loss of your company, and that of the rest of the Lunar Society.'

Before tracing the events that brought this happy interlude to a sudden end, we must take a closer look at the work Priestley achieved at Fair Hill. It reflects his interest in current affairs, in developments that were taking place in the growing iron industry, as well as in the advent of 'hot air' and hydrogen balloons—an unexpected result of the work on gases, and one for which the French gave much credit to Priestley, though he played no direct part in it. Several of his new experiments were carried out either in sunlight or in the focus of one of Parker's burning lenses. For this reason those who wished to see his latest work were advised: 'Come when the sun shines.'

Chapter 11

Science at Fair Hill

PRIESTLEY's strength as a scientist lay in his ability to devise simple apparatus and to manipulate it in so nimble a manner that a continual stream of new observations could be made. Though he did not regard himself primarily as a chemist, his work in the 1770s had so accustomed men of science to thinking in terms of the part played by the atmosphere and other gases in chemical reactions that, so to speak, a new dimension had been added to chemical thought. Much of this work had entailed the use and study of acids and metals, and by this new way of thinking a reinterpretation of many reactions, in particular those of metals and their compounds, became possible. As some of his contemporaries realized, this, among other things, was eventually to lead to a much deeper understanding of the whole field of metallurgy, including the extraction of the metals from their ores.

While at Calne, Priestley had shown that some striking reactions of metals and their salts depended on dephlogistication (that is, oxidation). For example, it was well known that copper dissolved in a solution of sal ammoniac to give a beautiful blue solution. By allowing this to take place in a closed bottle for a day or two, he was able to examine the air above the liquid, and found that it became progressively 'worse'. On one occasion it was almost completely phlogisticated, that is, in the future language of the French chemists, all the oxygen had been taken up.

It was also known that green solutions of iron salts turned red on standing. Priestley poured a dilute solution of pearl ashes (potassium carbonate) into a dilute solution of green vitriol (ferrous sulphate), using a funnel to avoid disturbing the air too much, and then inserting a stopper. The precipitate, he said, was at first light blue (or green), then a darker blue, and finally red. It became red at the surface first, indicating that the air was causing the change to take place. As in the previous experiment, the air became phlogisticated. The change was not due to loss of fixed air from the precipitate, for he took some of the fresh green precipitate and coated the inside of a glass tube with it, allowing it to stand over water for three weeks. The air in the tube was found to be completely phlogisticated, but no fixed air had been produced. On arrival at Birmingham, he explained these reactions, and showed that similar results were obtained with lime-water as alkali, and this contained no fixed air. In modern terms, he had demonstrated clearly that oxygen was absorbed when ferrous carbonate and hydroxide were oxidized to the corresponding ferric compounds.

Metals and Nitric Acid

In his volume of 1781, Priestley described further experiments on 'modified' nitrous air (nitrous oxide) which were the starting-point of Humphry Davy's researches some fifteen years later. This was the gas he had obtained when iron was exposed for a time to nitrous air (nitric oxide). He had noticed that solutions of iron salts turned black when nitrous air was bubbled into them, and suggested this as a test for iron compounds. Blue solutions of copper salts turned green.

He also noticed that when dilute nitric acid was poured into a bottle containing iron nails, the nitrous air produced was changed slowly to the form in which a candle burned with a vivid flame (nitrous oxide). When the metal was zinc, most of the gas produced right away was nitrous oxide, and so he tried to find a way of adapting this reaction to obtain the gas in a pure state. He discovered that it dissolved in water and was expelled from it on heating. This was the only way he could find to separate it from other nitrous airs, and it became a standard method of preparation. Tin gave similar results to zinc.

In studying the change from nitric oxide to nitrous oxide in the presence of iron nails, Priestley noted that the volume of the gas was reduced to one-half, though he made no attempt to explain this fact. As nitrous oxide supported combustion, he tried the effect of sparking a mixture of it with hydrogen and there was a 'considerably violent' explosion, as with a mixture of oxygen and hydrogen. He also noted that nitrous oxide changed to nitrogen in the presence of the iron filings and sulphur mixture, but the volume of gas was scarcely altered.

Having found that nitrous oxide could be produced from nitric oxide by several phlogistic processes, and that the same processes eventually changed nitrous oxide to nitrogen, one would expect that he would have called the nitrous oxide by the name of phlogisticated nitrous air. He did so at first, but then found that iron scales produced during the hammering of heated iron had the same effect as iron itself on nitrous air. Now iron scales were a calx of iron, and he thought that a calx could only take up phlogiston. And so the gas was known as *de*phlogisticated nitrous air until it was found that iron scales could, in fact, take up more oxygen and form another calx (ferric oxide). A further observation became of greater significance in the time of Davy, when nitrous oxide became known as 'laughing gas' and was later used as an anaesthetic in dentistry: Priestley found that a mouse could live in the gas, but only for five minutes.

In 1786 he published a final series of experiments on nitrous oxide, showing that the gas was composed of the same constituents as common air. On sparking a small quantity of the gas over mercury, he found that it was 'converted into ordinary air wholly immiscible with water' (that is, a mixture of oxygen and nitrogen). He had now revealed a chain of reactions that showed an intricate series of connections between air and nitric acid. That there was such a connection had been an idea that had haunted chemical thought for a long period, but only now was the reality made known. The last links were provided by Priestley and Cavendish during work on the composition of water, when it was found that the sparking of moist air led directly to the formation of nitric acid.

Iron and Steam

Before Priestley came to Birmingham, he had been interested in the way various substances corroded iron and glass, and how the effect could be accentuated when the substances were heated strongly in sealed tubes. Thus water, when heated in a sealed glass tube for several hours, became milky and deposited small flakes or powder (silica). This was not the conversion of water to earth, as some chemists, such as Peter Woulfe, still believed, but a true corrosion of the glass, which afterwards was found to have lost its polish on the inside surface and to be pitted.

Priestley had noted a similar result when water was heated in a sealed gun-barrel, though then the tube was eventually worn right through; but on opening it before this point was reached he found a considerable amount of rust. However, the air in the tube had scarcely changed, and presumably had not taken part in the reaction. Not long after this, the action of steam on iron was being studied by Priestley in Birmingham and by Lavoisier and others in France. In 1784 Lavoisier and Meusnier published an experiment in which inflammable air (hydrogen) was obtained from the action of water on iron. They coated a gun-barrel with clay and heated it in a furnace, inclining it so that water could drip slowly into it from a tin funnel placed at the top end. Any steam coming out at the bottom of the gun-barrel was condensed in a spiral tube, and the emerging inflammable gas was collected in a pneumatic trough. The account appeared at a time when chemists generally were puzzling over the question of the constitution of water.

Priestley probably learned of the new method of making hydrogen on a visit to London in the spring of 1784, when he attended meetings of the Royal Society for the reading of papers by Watt on the composition of water, and by Withering on experiments with *terra ponderosa* (baryta). On 23 April, Banks wrote to tell Watt that his paper had been read the previous day, and mentioned that Priestley was there. 'How much the Royal Society and the world at large are indebted in Point of Science to the town of Birmingham I need not declare after mentioning him. . . .' On 11 May, Banks wrote again to tell him that a postscript to his paper had also been read and that the French 'mode of making inflammable air by passing the steam of water through redhot Iron' had been received. A copy of the paper was sent to Priestley by Lavoisier.

Watt was necessarily interested in any action between steam and iron, but Priestley's economical mind turned rather to the possibility of making cheap hydrogen to fill the new 'aerostatic' balloons that had been invented in France and had been flown in this country in the previous autumn. Fordyce had been commissioned to fill the first such balloon to be seen in London, and he had used zinc and sulphuric acid. The process was expensive, and it was necessary to keep the cost down as much as possible. Fordyce considered the various methods available and the value of the chemical by-products on the market, and decided on zinc, for the white vitriol produced would fetch about £400 and was more easily sold than the more common green vitriol obtained from iron. Priestley thought that scrap iron and steam offered a much cheaper way altogether, and returned to Birmingham with ideas for testing the method.

With the help of Watt and Galton he tried iron tubes of varying diameter, but as these soon became corroded and leaked he later tried enclosing pieces of iron in copper tubes. The results of this work were first communicated to the French, and the reasons for this should perhaps be clarified.

Magellan seems to have been his first link with the continent of Europe, but Priestley's relations with France were strengthened considerably during his tour of 1774 and by his meetings with Frenchmen who were guests of Lord Shelburne. After going to Birmingham, he made more use of overseas friends who were visiting England, and up to 1782 he was helped by Franklin's presence in France.

Priestley also became acquainted with the French journalist and politician, J. P. Brissot de Warville, who visited London in 1782–4 and met him at Kirwan's house. Brissot was surprised that Priestley's work had not made such a great impact in England as it had in France. He was also impressed by the man's human qualities, particularly on learning that the chief reason for Priestley's journey to London on that occasion had been an educational one—to show his son Joseph the launching of a ship at Deptford.[1]

On 26 February 1784 Priestley had been elected an *associé étranger* of the Paris Academy of Sciences, a vacancy having

[1] *Mémoires de Brissot*, Paris, 1830, ii, 263–7, 320.

occurred through the death of Wargentin, Secretary of the Stockholm Academy.

During the Revolution the French admitted, for reasons that now seem obscure, that their pre-eminence in ballooning was due largely to Priestley's work. This may have been partly an impression due to his great reputation in France as a leader of liberal thought, but even the Montgolfier brothers owed something to their reading of Priestley's early volumes. The most likely reason for this appears to be that in his account of different kinds of air he emphasized the differences in densities of different gases, and in particular showed that phlogisticated air, alkaline air, and especially inflammable air were appreciably less dense than common air. The first Montgolfier balloons were, indeed, filled with the aid of quick-burning straw and chopped wool, which were thought to produce alkaline air, but it was soon found that the effect was due to an inward rush of hot air. Not long afterwards, hydrogen was used instead of hot air. Though the measurement of the density of hydrogen had been made by Cavendish, it was Priestley's book that brought the facts to the notice of the French.

In September 1784 Priestley was visited by another Frenchman, Faujas de St Fond, whom he allowed to take a drawing of his new apparatus 'for the purpose of communicating it to the French chemists who are engaged in the same pursuit . . .'. On entering Priestley's laboratory, he was struck by the simple and ingenious apparatus for making experiments on 'inflammable gas extracted from iron and water reduced to vapour' (Fig. 9).

The tube, which was thick and long, was made of red copper and cast in one piece to avoid joinings. The part exposed to the fire was thicker than the rest. Into this tube he introduced cuttings or filings of iron, and instead of dropping in the water he preferred making it enter in vapour. The furnace destined for this operation was supplied with coke made of coal, which is the best of all combustibles for the intensity and equality of its heat. By these means he obtained a considerable quantity of inflammable gas of great lightness and without any smell. He observed to me, that by increasing the apparatus and using iron or copper tubes of a large calibre, aerostatic balloons might be filled with far less trouble and expense than by vitriolic acid.

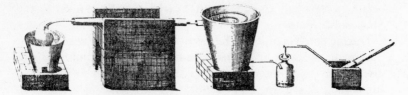

Fig. 9 Apparatus for preparing hydrogen by passing steam over red-hot iron in a copper tube (not to scale). For filling balloons, the gas issuing from the tube was to be passed through water into a large inverted funnel, and piped off.

Whether this reaction, as Lavoisier believed, did in fact show that water was being decomposed was a question which Priestley was slow to answer. He explained his characteristic point of view to Faujas de St Fond as follows:

The decomposition of water is of so much importance in Natural Philosophy, and would occupy so distinguished a place among the phenomena of the universe, that far from admitting the fact upon slight evidence, and as it were from enthusiasm, it were rather to be wished that all objections that may be made, and which will still long continue to be made against this theory were completely refuted; in the conflict of opinions, truth may at last be obtained. But I have still so many doubts upon this subject, and I have so many experiments to make both *pro* and *con*, that I can as yet regard the greatest as only started.

Priestley's attitude has been so often treated with scant respect by his own countrymen that it is refreshing to find a foreigner understanding his point of view so clearly and saying nothing to suggest that it was in any way unreasonable. Priestley was perhaps correct in regarding the composition of water as providing a crucial problem of interpretation for the new chemistry.

The Composition of Water

The first experiment that, in Cavendish's hands, led eventually to knowledge of the composition of water was carried out by Priestley not later than the spring of 1781 as 'a mere random experiment, made to entertain a few philosophical friends, who had formed themselves into a private society, of which they had done me the honour to make me a member'—apparently a reference to his colleagues of the Lunar Society. Priestley had not considered it of sufficient importance to be included in the text of the volume then going to press, and it only appeared in the form of a letter from Warltire dated 18 April 1781. Warltire had been in Birmingham for some time giving public courses of lectures on science and was on friendly terms with most members of the Lunar Society, whose meetings he seems to have attended in preparation for the course advertised to begin on 19 March 1781.

Mr. Warltire's Course of twelve Philosophical Lectures, with the necessary Experiments, is to be opened on Monday the 19th Instant, at Six in the Evening, in the large Room at the Coffee House, in Cherry-Street, Birmingham. . . . New Discoveries are taken Notice of, and their Connection shewn with former Improvements.

In his letter, Warltire had described how he had used Priestley's demonstration of the sparking of inflammable air

Fig. 10 Apparatus for sparking mixtures of hydrogen and oxygen.

with common air (Fig. 10) in an attempt to discover whether heat had weight. What proved to be the most important observation was added almost as an afterthought:

I have fired air in *glass* vessels since I saw you venture to do it, and have observed, as you did, that though the glass was clean and dry before, yet after firing the air, it became dewy, and was lined with a sooty substance.

Warltire, in the presence of Priestley and Withering, had repeatedly sparked mixtures of inflammable and common air in a copper vessel supplied with a screw stopper, and when he afterwards blew out the 'phlogisticated air' it was seen to be smoking. In these experiments the copper vessel appeared to have lost weight, but Priestley did not feel convinced by the result. 'I do not think . . . that so very bold an opinion, as that of the latent heat of bodies contributing to their weight, should be received without more experiments.' As regards the random experiment Priestley had shown to his friends, he said:

After we had fired the mixture of *common* and inflammable air, we did the same with *dephlogisticated* and inflammable air; and though, in this case, the light was much more intense, and the heat much greater, the explosion was not so violent, but that a glass tube about an inch in diameter, and not exceeding one tenth of an inch in thickness, bore it without injury.

In this explosion, Priestley said, there is a great diminution of the bulk of the air, so that it is quite different from the firing of gunpowder, in which much air is produced.

At that time none of them thought the production of steam or water of much consequence, Warltire supposing that air deposits any moisture it contains when phlogisticated. Thus none of them knew how to interpret these results, and it was not until the spring of 1783 that Cavendish, carefully weighing the gases and the water produced, could even state them correctly. When hydrogen and air are exploded in the proper proportions, he said, the hydrogen reacts with about a fifth of the air (namely, the oxygen); they lose their elasticity and condense to form the dew that lines the vessel. Despite this, Cavendish believed that the water produced had pre-existed in the hydrogen and oxygen, so that the discovery of the true composition of water still eluded him.

But before this point had been reached, Priestley, following up one of Watt's ideas, had carried out some experiments that at first seemed to show that water could be converted into permanent air. Priestley argued that if water could be held in combination with some other substance so that it could be heated strongly, its particles might repel each other so strongly that it would take up the form of a permanently elastic fluid. He therefore took boiled water, combined it with lime, and heated the product to red heat in an earthenware retort. He got no steam, but a large quantity of air in which a candle would just burn. On 8 December 1782 he wrote to Wedgwood to announce the result of the experiment, but already by 8 January 1783 he was writing again to say that this did not happen when he used a glass retort. This enabled Wedgwood to offer a clue to the explanation, for it was possible that air was coming into the earthenware retort from outside or from the fire. Had Priestley accepted this explanation, some of the later confusion might have been avoided. On 23 January he replied to Wedgwood that he did not know what to make of his results: 'I have a tolerably good habit of circumspection with respect to *facts*; but as to *conclusions* from them, I am not apt to be very confident.'

Soon afterwards he learnt of Cavendish's experiments, which he called 'the re-conversion of air into water, by decomposing it in conjunction with inflammable air'. Clearly he did not regard it as his own discovery, although Cavendish had used Priestley's and Warltire's experiments as his starting-point. In order to test this new view of the matter, Priestley decided that it would be necessary to make sure that the dephlogisticated air and the inflammable air never came into contact with water. He therefore made the former from nitre and the latter by heating charcoal. This again was unfortunate, as neither of the gases obtained was anything like pure enough for the purpose. When the mixture was fired electrically, water was produced— about the same quantity as would be expected if the gases had been kept for a time over water. He attempted to weigh the water formed by collecting it from the inside of the vessel on a weighed filter-paper. In this experiment the impurities formed soluble by-products, and he found, although he admitted that his balance was scarcely sensitive enough for certainty in the matter, that the weight of the air that had vanished in the explosion was the same as the weight of the moisture collected on the filter-paper. He told Watt of these results, and on 23 March wrote also to Wedgwood about them.

By this time Priestley was becoming suspicious about his water-into-air experiments, and by the end of the month he had made arrangements to go to London in order to try out some modifications with Parker's large burning glass, which confirmed to his satisfaction that air had entered the retort from outside. He was therefore rather surprised, and perhaps chagrined, to receive from Watt a letter dated 26 April 1783, in which he attempted to explain both sets of results—the conversion of water into air, and the re-conversion of air into

water. The first set was wrong, and the second far from satisfactory, and so it is doubtful how much credit should go to Watt
for producing explanations that came very near to the truth.
After summarizing the 'facts' as Priestley had reported them,
Watt asked:

Are we not then authorized to conclude that Water is composed
of dephlogisticated air and inflammable air, or phlogiston, deprived
of part of their latent or elementary heat and that dephlogisticated
or pure air, is composed of water deprived of its phlogiston and
united to elementary heat and light and thus the latter are contained
in it in a latent state so as not to be sensible to the thermometer or
to the eye.

Here Watt seemed to be identifying hydrogen with phlogiston
—as did Priestley and Kirwan for a time—but in the water-
into-air experiments there was no liberation of hydrogen. By
this time Priestley knew that water had not been converted into
air, and so, sending Watt a diagram of the apparatus he had
used to discover this, he replied on 29 April:

Behold with surprize and with indignation the figure of an
apparatus that has utterly ruined your beautiful hypothesis, and has
rendered some weeks of my labour . . . almost useless.

He had enclosed a retort in a large bell-jar standing over
water, the neck of the retort being attached to a receiver
(Fig. 11). He then heated the retort from outside with a large
burning lens; as he did so, the water level in the bell-jar rose,
showing that air had passed into the retort; and at the same
time air passed into the receiver.

By 1 May, Priestley was discussing this latest development
with his friends, some of whom were by now thoroughly
mystified. On 2 May, Magellan wrote to Young:

Our good friend is now in London: and he told me yesterday, that
the experiments lately made, with the burning lens of Parker, as far
as I could understand him, convinced him that there was not a real
conversion of water into air. . . .

The matter was being discussed that very evening at an informal
meeting of the Royal Society. A note added to the letter on

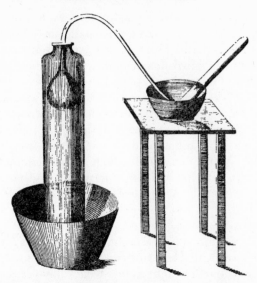

Fig. 11 Apparatus to show the 'seeming conversion' of water into air.

13 May said that Priestley's new experiments showed that fire opens the pores of bodies and passes through some of them along with the surrounding air. Priestley showed Watt's letter to Sir Joseph Banks, then President of the Royal Society, but in view of these developments Watt asked that it should not be read to the Society at that time.

The paper in which Cavendish announced his complete results was not read until 15 January 1784; in it he discussed them in terms of the views of Priestley and his friends. He said:

> I think we must allow that dephlogisticated air is in reality nothing but dephlogisticated water, or water deprived of its phlogiston; or, in other words, that water consists of dephlogisticated air united to phlogiston; and that inflammable air is either pure phlogiston, as Dr. Priestley and Mr. Kirwan suppose, or else water united to phlogiston.

Watt considered that this closely resembled his own views, and so he now asked for his letter to Priestley of 26 April 1783 to be read to the Society, and this was subsequently done (p. 151).

At the time of Cavendish's paper (January 1784) Priestley

wrote to Wedgwood—with a passing allusion to the new application of gas chemistry to aerostatic balloons—that the 'great
problem with us aerial philosophers (not navigators) is what
happens when dephlogisticated and inflammable airs *unite* by
explosion &c'. The products seemed to vary—depending on the
proportions of the reacting gases, the sources from which they
were obtained, and whether common air or dephlogisticated air
were used—from pure water, to water and fixed air, and water
contaminated with nitric acid. He was now aware that the
inflammable air from charcoal, which he had used himself, was
different from the gas obtained from metals and vitriolic acid,
and he described for Wedgwood's benefit how he had found
this out.

Iron filings, heated in oxygen with a burning lens, took in the
oxygen and became 'scales of iron', as in a smith's forge. If the
scales were now heated in hydrogen, the latter disappeared and
the iron lost as much weight as one would have expected if the
hydrogen and oxygen had united. The weight of water produced
was also in agreement with this explanation. On the other hand,
if he used inflammable air from charcoal, fixed air (as well as
water) was produced.

Referring to the water-into-air experiments, Priestley had
now proved to his own satisfaction that steam passed through
the pores of the retort in one direction while air passed through
in the opposite direction. With the aid of an air-pump even
mercury could be forced through in tiny particles to emerge
as a black powder. Any gas could be used in place of common
air, and the result would be the same. Some critics, who fail
to give the sequel to these experiments, think that Priestley
was wrong to publish them as soon as he did. But they
were of wide interest to scientists for almost two decades,
when Dalton was able to explain them by means of his theory
of diffusion. 'The fact of air passing into the retort through
its pores, and vapour out of them at the same time,' he wrote,
'are elegantly and most convincingly shewn by Dr. Priestley's
experiments.'

Wedgwood was then in London, and Priestley asked that he
would convey these results to Kirwan and Banks. In a further
letter of 23 January 1784 Priestley referred to the 'water

controversy', meaning by this the discussion of Watt's current view that air was dephlogisticated water (he said originally that *pure* air, or oxygen, was dephlogisticated water). Priestley did not feel directly concerned with this, thinking that his part was to keep on supplying additional experimental evidence so that the truth could be arrived at more easily. 'In this business I am little more than the *bellows blower*,' he said.

He had now found another complication, for iron (from which inflammable air was generally obtained) was by no means a simple or constant substance. Cast iron, he said, dissolves in acids with great difficulty, and requires annealing before it will dissolve readily. Steel, unlike malleable iron, contains a good deal of insoluble matter, much of which is phlogiston (carbon). But at this stage his work was interrupted by an accident—'a phial of hot oil of vitriol having exploded, spoiled my clothes, & burnt my hand; so that I shall not be able to do anything in the laboratory for some days'.

Chemistry and the Iron Industry

Many other experiments and attempts to understand the various phenomena associated with iron, carbon, and steam, which were becoming of increasing importance and interest to manufacturers, were carried out in 1784 and later, and the most important of these were described in his final volume published in 1786.

William Lewis had shown in his *Philosophical Commerce of Arts* (1763–5) that many industrial problems could be studied scientifically and that chemistry could throw much light on the nature of a metal such as platinum. After this he had turned his attention to iron and in 1767–70 had made considerable progress with his project for the 'Chemical and Mineral History of Iron'. Much of the collection of material and the drafting had been the responsibility of Lewis's assistant, Alexander Chisholm, who subsequently entered Wedgwood's service after Lewis's death in 1781. Chisholm was known to Priestley, who refers to him in letters to Wedgwood in 1782 and later, and so Priestley may well have known of this project. But Chisholm's knowledge could not have been of much help to him, for what stands out most clearly in Lewis's manuscript [1] is the absence of any indication of the part played by gases in the reactions of iron. He was aware of Cavendish's work on hydrogen, but Priestley's papers on different kinds of air had not been written at that time. Lewis was also aware that various 'vapours' were formed when acids acted on iron, and he had proposed to 'catch' the vapours produced when iron was heated with strong vitriolic acid (Priestley's vitriolic acid air) and when calx of iron was heated with charcoal. But there is no record to show that his resources were adequate for these tasks.

That chemists could now tackle such questions shows the importance of the advances in technique that had since been made. Priestley had fairly clear ideas about the reaction between steam and iron. For the time being, at any rate, he acquiesced in the view that steam was composed of dephlogisticated air and inflammable air. The metal took the dephlogisticated air and formed a calx. The inflammable air was set free.

Experiments were then made with charcoal and steam, but the results were less satisfactory and more variable. The products were fixed air and inflammable air. He removed the fixed air with lime-water, and fired the inflammable air with an equal volume of dephlogisticated air, which should have been sufficient to act with the whole of it. At that time neither he nor Lavoisier was prepared for the result, since he obtained, not water, but a further considerable quantity of fixed air. Not knowing that charcoal and oxygen could combine to form an inflammable gas (carbon monoxide) he concluded, reasonably enough, that this fixed air had been combined with the inflammable air, and so referred to it as 'combined fixed air'. The method did not enable him to detect the main products of the reaction: uncombined fixed air (carbon dioxide), combined fixed air (carbon monoxide), and inflammable air (hydrogen). He made a number of guesses as to what had happened. Finally, referring to the origin of the combined fixed air, he said: 'whether the charcoal only supplies the phlogiston, and the water its basis, that is, dephlogisticated air, deserves to be investigated'.

At this time Priestley was sending frequent notes by his

[1] Cardiff Reference Library, MS. 3.250, 6 vols.

house-boy to Watt's house at Harper's Hill. One of these, marked 'Fair Hill. Sunday morning', is preserved at Birmingham. It gives information about inflammable and fixed air from charcoal, and contains comments on data sent to Watt on two previous occasions. Clearly he felt the need of Watt's advice, for in a postscript he invited himself, with his wife and daughter, to take a dish of tea with the Watts that afternoon.

Though the facts of the reaction between charcoal and steam had been described accurately, Priestley had failed to find a satisfactory explanation. It might therefore be thought that little would have been gained by his proceeding to the question of how calx of iron (iron scales, or finery cinder, as it was known to the ironmasters) reacted with charcoal. He knew that inflammable air reacted with scales of iron, reviving the metal and producing water. Hydrogen and charcoal were both forms of phlogiston, and so he expected similar results.

The scales of iron (magnetic iron oxide, Fe_3O_4) and the charcoal were first heated separately to ensure that they contained no air, and then mixed while still hot and placed in an airtight retort—glazed inside and out. The retort was then placed in a furnace and connected with a condenser and a vessel to receive the water that was expected.

But, to my great surprise, not one particle of *moisture* came over, but a prodigious quantity of *air*, and the rapidity of its production astonished me; so that I had no doubt but that the weight of the air would have been equal to the loss of weight both in the scales and the charcoal; and when I examined the air, which I repeatedly did, I found it to contain one-tenth of fixed air, and the inflammable air, which remained when the fixed air was separated from it, was of a very remarkable kind, being quite as heavy as common air. The reason of this was sufficiently apparent when it was decomposed by means of dephlogisticated air; for the greatest part of it was fixed air.

He reported these results to Wedgwood on 8 November 1784, and there is little doubt that he had prepared fairly pure specimens of carbon monoxide, for he said that only the first portions of the gas coming over contained free fixed air, the last none at all.

The reason why he did not recognize that he had prepared a new air seems to be that he thought there could be only one 'inflammable air', though it appeared in various guises, just as phlogiston itself could appear in forms as different as hydrogen and carbon. It was from this kind of thought that Keir attempted to wean him. He tried to convince him that 'there is not one inflammable but many inflammables, which opinion you now think as heterodox as the Athanasian System'. Nevertheless, the letter in which Keir made this comment reveals that he also lacked any clear ideas on the subject.

Priestley then decided to try the effect of heating iron in other gases than oxygen and steam, and made two notable observations. Vitriolic acid air (sulphur dioxide) was absorbed by iron just as rapidly as dephlogisticated air, but the iron melted more readily. The inside of the vessel became covered with a sooty matter, and this was shown to be sulphur, as it sublimed to a white vapour, leaving the glass clean. The iron had become brittle, and presumably *sulphurated*, as the ironmasters termed it.

When iron was heated in nitrous air (nitric oxide) it was changed to 'finery cinder', and phlogisticated air remained in the vessel. Thus, as he informed Wedgwood, nitrous air, dephlogisticated air, and steam 'all contain the same common principle, and nitrous air appears to be a compound of pure air and phlogisticated air'.

Towards the end of the book Priestley pointed out that although iron was the most important metal, it was still imperfectly understood, both by chemists and ironmasters. All new facts should be reported, for they might be of use to large-scale manufacturers. Among the problems that needed elucidation were the reasons for the great differences in properties between cast iron, malleable iron, annealed iron, and steel, which he showed were related in some way to the amount of foreign matter in the iron. This was left behind after the specimen had been dissolved in vitriolic acid. He heated these residuums *in vacuo* and in the open air, and showed that they consisted mainly of plumbago (carbon). One specimen, for example, contained 13 parts of plumbago in 19, the other six forming a glassy slag. Cast iron gave the largest residue.

Again, from his reading about ironmaking he received the impression that the change from cast iron to malleable iron was due to hammering while red-hot. But on seeing the process he

Plate 13 Matthew Boulton's Soho Manufactory towards the end of the eighteenth century. An engraving by Francis Eginton, one of the artists employed by Boulton for painting japan ware and copying works of art.

Plate 14 One of Sayers' cartoons, published in Feburary 1790, shortly before the third application for the Repeal of the Test Act. Priestley is shown in the pulpit with Price and Lindsey (indicated by the letters PPL). Below them are (*left*) Charles James Fox and (*right*) the Earl of Stanhope. (*British Museum*)

realized that the air-blast used to heat the cast iron was the important factor, for during this heating most of the liquid matter, or finery cinder, was separated. The loose, spongy masses that remained were then consolidated by the hammer, and more finery cinder was removed. Uses should be found for the finery cinder, which was often allowed to run away, as being of no value. Some, indeed, was used in the best bottle-glass, and Wilkinson for several years had been returning a proportion for re-smelting. This cinder, Priestley found, consisted mainly of the same calx that was produced by the action of steam on iron. It could be converted to iron again by means of heat in the presence of hydrogen, charcoal, coke, or raw coal.

The cementation process was not properly understood by the steel-makers or by the annealers of cast iron. The former thought there was no alteration in weight in the change from malleable iron to steel, and the annealers, who heated cast iron in a bed of charcoal, thought there was a considerable loss in weight. Priestley challenged both these views, though his own experiments were inconclusive. Similar work was being done by others on the Continent, especially Berthollet and Guyton de Morveau.

Different Kinds of Inflammable Air

By the time he came to write his sixth volume (1786) Priestley was convinced that, even if there were only one inflammable principle, namely phlogiston, there were several 'different kinds of inflammable air', and a section of the book contained this phrase in its title. He described numerous preparations of inflammable airs from various substances, and characterized three distinct inflammable gases—hydrogen, carbon monoxide, and hydrogen sulphide, as they are now called. The first two were distinguished by the difference in the way they burned, in their specific gravities, and in their reactions with oxygen. Since 1784 his views on 'combined fixed air', obtained by heating scales of iron with charcoal, had changed, and it so happens that the same book contains not only his 'discovery' of combined fixed air but also his later views, which led him to cancel both the name and the ideas that gave rise to it. He had,

12

indeed, followed the argument from the specific gravity of the gas to its logical conclusion, and had found that the new gas could not possibly have been fixed air combined with hydrogen. He also examined the reaction of the gas with oxygen more carefully, giving the ratios by volume. In three results, one measure of the gas gave 0·9, 0·94, and 1 measure of fixed air, respectively. This, he said, was a clear proof that the fixed air could not have been present originally in a combined state. He did not make the simple inference that all of the gas had gone into the composition of the fixed air, but, arguing from their specific gravities, showed that any result greater than 0·7 would have been a 'proof that at least part of that fixed air was generated in the process'.

He also appears to have wondered whether this was the same inflammable air that he had obtained in the early days when he tried to make fixed air by heating chalk in a gun-barrel (p. 70). On heating fixed air in a gun-barrel he now obtained this heavy inflammable air. He likewise heated slaked lime, but the inflammable gas on that occasion was the lighter one (produced from steam and iron).

Priestley's discovery of hydrogen sulphide similarly resulted from his experiments with steam passed over various solids heated in tubes. Peter Woulfe had sent him a specimen of manganese, and on passing steam over it he obtained an inflammable gas with a strong smell of 'liver of sulphur'. On standing over water, the gas gave a deposit which he recognized as sulphur. He did not get this gas from other specimens of manganese, and so concluded that it had been produced from an impurity present. He next came across the gas unexpectedly. He wanted to make a large quantity of hydrogen, and for this purpose used the iron that had previously been heated in vitriolic acid air, and consequently was 'sulphurated'. Dilute oil of vitriol on this gave the same gas as before, and the jars 'were presently black as ink, but became yellow when exposed to the open air'. For the future this was the method of preparation he employed, the 'sulphurated' iron being made by dipping red-hot iron into molten sulphur.

The Charcoal of Metals

The technique of passing vapours and gases through tubes of iron, copper, or earthenware had well repaid the attention Priestley had given it. In the course of this work he discovered what would today be called the catalytic decomposition of alcohol vapour in the presence of copper or silver. He descriptively, but inappropriately, called this the preparation of the 'charcoal of metals'. Priestley found that the metals played a very real, although unusual, part in these reactions, the first of which was reported to Wedgwood in a letter of 8 November 1784. He had passed alcohol vapour through a heated copper tube, and had obtained water, inflammable air, no fixed air, and a considerable amount of a black powder, afterwards shown to be the same as charcoal. The copper tube had perished.

Because of this, he transferred pieces of copper to an earthenware tube, heated it to keep them just melted, and passed alcohol vapour over them. Though he had used two ounces of copper, it lost no more than 28 grains while 446 grains of charcoal were deposited in the tube. In another trial he made 508 grains of charcoal for the loss of only 19 grains of copper. He noted that 'the minute division, and volatility of this charcoal, is very extraordinary'. This charcoal was insoluble in acids and burned rapidly in oxygen to produce fixed air. Apparently he thought that in some way the discovery might be of significance in coining, a subject of considerable interest at the time not only to Wilkinson, but even more so to Boulton and Watt. For example, in 1786 the latter succeeded in fulfilling an order for 100 tons of copper coinage for the East India Company.

Whatever the line of thought may have been, the fact remains that with some kind of intuition the next metal he tried was silver, and he found the result very much the same. If this charcoal could be produced in profusion from copper and silver, what would be the effect of gold? He found that it was not affected.

Finding this process to have so remarkable an effect upon copper, and none at all upon gold, I imagined that by this means, it might be possible to separate copper from gold, so that we should be in possession of a new and effectual mode of *assaying*. But I was disappointed in this expectation. I mixed ten grains of copper with an hundred of gold; but the copper was effectually protected by the gold from the action of the spirit of wine, and the whole mass came out of the same weight that it had before it was subjected to the experiment.

He then tried lead, tin, and iron, but with very little effect. With turpentine the results were similar.

If, as his friends at Manchester said, his work was of importance to the arts, to commerce, and to science, why was it that at this time some of his subscribers began to fall away? As he was so successful as an experimenter, they could not understand why he did not give his whole time to scientific work. Priestley himself gave the answer. He felt that the state of the country and the world demanded that his greatest exertions should be made in serving the cause of religion and liberty, and by 1786 science had begun to take second place. But he had not lost his keenness, for he wrote:

I view with rapture the glorious face of nature, and I admire its wonderful constitution, the laws of which are daily unfolding themselves to our view. It is but little that the life of man permits us to see at present, and therefore I feel a most eager desire to renew my acquaintance with it hereafter, and to resume those inquiries with which I am so much delighted now, and which must be interrupted by death. . . .

Such discoveries as these, give us a higher idea of the value of our being, by raising our ideas of the system of which we are a part. . . .

Besides, civil society is but in its infancy, the world itself is but very imperfectly known to the civilized inhabitants of it, and we are but little acquainted with the real value of those few of its productions of which we have some knowledge, and which we are only beginning to name, and to arrange. How must a citizen of the world wish to know the future progress of it.

Chapter 12

The Train of Gunpowder

To UNDERSTAND how it was that Priestley's interesting researches came almost to an end with the completion of his sixth volume, we must go back a few years and pick up the threads of his other activities. In December 1780, after he had settled in at Fair Hill, Priestley received a unanimous invitation to become minister of the New Meeting, Birmingham, the holder of that position having resigned. His cup of happiness was now full. He had a thriving congregation, and a colleague to relieve him of all but Sunday duties. Into this one day a week, however, he packed not only services, but also the three kinds of classes he had introduced at Leeds (p. 37). His method of instruction had been improved, and he was soon writing to his publisher for copies of his charts of biography and history for use in this work. The classes were well attended, and they played an important part in the development of Sunday schools in the town.

Allied to this was his interest in the public subscription library, which had been formed a year before his arrival, and to which he gave considerable support. He put it on a more business-like basis and helped in working out a new set of rules. Library meetings began to be advertised in Aris's *Birmingham Gazette*. For example, subscribers were called to a meeting on 13 June 1781, to consider its future management. The library, according to the advertisement, was still in its infancy, and had been formed 'on the plan of one first established in Liverpool and which has been adopted at Manchester, Leeds, and many other considerable towns'. Some years later Priestley had occasion to remind the subscribers that their rules, which were modelled on those of Leeds, and all their advertisements in the press, had been drawn up by himself. When helping with the selection of books, he always voted for everything that had been

written against him, but never for his own works. He preferred
that the business of the library should be dealt with by a small
committee, for 'it is well known . . . that nothing can be
discussed to advantage in a large assembly'.

He was now fully engaged in a multiplicity of activities after
his own heart, and he quickly became influential, though living
quietly. His arrival, indeed, was sufficiently noteworthy to be
mentioned by William Hutton, whose *History of Birmingham* was
in the press. Religion played its full part in the town, as it did
in the three other most important industrial centres in the
provinces—Manchester, Leeds, and Sheffield. Altogether there
were fourteen places of worship; six belonged to the established
Church, and all other prominent sects were represented. The
Church of St Philip, reminiscent of St Paul's, was the pride of
the place, said Hutton.

The New Meeting was erected in 1730, in what was considered an elegant style, and it had few equals in its class. The
Old Meeting, which had close relations with the New, was built
in the time of William III, a still older one having become a
workshop. In general, the various chapels of the Dissenters
compared unfavourably with those of the established Church.
Thus Carr's Lane Meeting was situated in a narrow street and
was 'surrounded with about forty families of paupers . . .
which amply furnish the congregation with noise, smoak, dirt
and dispute'. Other sects had their difficulties; the Methodists,
for example, were occupying a disused theatre, 'where they
continue to exhibit'. Priestley had been called to the most
respectable of the Dissenting congregations in Birmingham, and
probably the most liberal in England.

Soon he was engaged once more on his religious writings.
The New Meeting supported him with a gift of £200 towards
printing expenses, though he suspected that it was a cloak for
Russell's personal generosity. In a short while new publications
began to appear from his pen. Apart from some controversial
letters with which he was already occupied, his main efforts
were being devoted to a new edition of the *Institutes of Natural
and Revealed Religion* (1782), and especially the long-delayed
fourth volume, which now took the form of a separate work
entitled *An History of the Corruptions of Christianity*, produced in

two volumes at the same time. These were accompanied by second editions of his chief metaphysical works. Now that all Priestley's main teachings appeared at once, their impact seems to have been much greater than before.

In his *History* he tried to trace everything that he regarded as a corruption of early Christianity to its source. In general, he thought, he had been successful in showing how prevailing conditions and opinions had made the introduction of such changes appear sufficiently natural to have been adopted without much opposition. 'And if I have succeeded in this investigation, this *historical method* will be found to be one of the most satisfactory modes of argumentation, in order to prove that what I object to is really a corruption of genuine chris- tianity, and no part of the original scheme.' It was scarcely to be expected that one man in one book could answer all the questions that have occupied theological scholars and textual critics for many generations, but the value of the method he introduced has been acknowledged by several scholars.

His conclusion was drawn up in two parts, the first addressed to 'unbelievers, and especially to Mr. Gibbon', who had recently produced the first three volumes of his classic work, the *Decline and Fall*. Gibbon had been sarcastic about early Christianity, on which he had blamed the downfall of Rome, and this had caused offence in many quarters. Priestley gave him a public challenge to defend his opinions:

Now, though I am far from holding myself out as the champion of christianity, against all the world, I own I shall have no objection to discuss this subject with Mr. Gibbon, as an historian, and a philosopher. We are only two individuals, and no other persons can be bound by the result of our discussion.

Gibbon declined the invitation, calling Priestley a greater unbeliever than himself. He also advised Priestley to take a warning from the fate of Servetus who, despite his valuable discoveries in science, had been burnt at the stake as a heretic. To this Priestley replied:

I admire Servetus . . . more for his courage in dying for the cause of important truth, than I should have done if, besides the certain discovery of the circulation of the blood, he had made any other the most celebrated discovery in philosophy.

This was in February 1783. Relations quickly worsened, and
Priestley's final note to him, on 25 February, was curt and
pointed: 'Mr. Gibbon may easily escape all further altercation,
by discontinuing this mutually disagreeable correspondence,
and leaving Dr. Priestley to act as his own discretion, or
indiscretion, may dictate.'

In the second part of his conclusion, Priestley had addressed
his remarks to 'advocates for the present civil establishments and
especially to Bishop Hurd'. Though he had failed to bring
Gibbon out into the open, he had no cause to be dissatisfied
with the outcome of his second challenge, for it produced a
skilful and vigorous attack from Samuel Horsley, Archdeacon
of St Alban's. Priestley replied, with the result that one of the
fiercest controversies of the age was fought for several years,
Horsley's attacks being mixed with what he admitted to be
'intemperate wrath and carnal anger'.

To understand the importance of Horsley's intervention, it
must be remembered that he, like Priestley, had divided his
time between religion and science, and that from 1773 to 1778
he had been secretary of the Royal Society. Before that he had
been tutor to the Earl of Aylesford's eldest son, who was shortly
to play a significant part in Warwickshire affairs. From 1776
to 1784 Horsley was engaged in producing an edition of
Newton's philosophical works, which gave him greater standing
in the world of science. As one who could not hide his hatred
of Dissenters, Horsley found himself, in 1783, in conflict not
only with Priestley, but also with Sir Joseph Banks, whose
conduct as President he called into question. By this time
Horsley's former pupil, now Earl of Aylesford, who had been
elected to the Royal Society at a very early age, had been made
a member of the Privy Council.

Horsley did not attempt to answer Priestley's arguments or to
assess the validity of the historical method. Instead he set out
to destroy the authority of Priestley's name, which had risen
high in the public esteem through what were now called 'lucky'
scientific discoveries. He cited instances of arguing in a circle,
misapplied quotations, forced constructions, ignorance of Pla-
tonic philosophy, and so on. Priestley took little notice of this,
which he privately regarded as insolent and unworthy of the

man, but tried to draw Horsley into a 'tedious controversy on the main question'; but Horsley's refusal to be drawn, on the grounds that the subject had been long ago exhausted, did not help his case. By the autumn of 1784 Priestley had found examples in his opponent's letters of insufficient knowledge of the subject, of misrepresentation, of falsifying history for his own ends, and of defaming the character of a church father.

In the middle of this exchange, Priestley published a more than usually outspoken pamphlet based on a sermon preached on 5 November 1785. It was concerned with *The Importance and Extent of Free Enquiry*, and he again maintained that several of the so-called cardinal doctrines of the Reformers were in reality doctrines of the church of Rome, which Luther and Calvin left as they found them. It is our fault if we go no further, he said. To ensure that his pamphlets met with some response, he often added challenging remarks, and this time he seems to have made mental play with the date. At all events, he introduced a gunpowder simile—against the advice of Wedgwood, who correctly forecast that it would make too much noise—and this gave his enemies a weapon they refused to lay down. In its context, however, it now seems harmless enough.

Let us not, therefore, be discouraged, though, for the present, we should see no great number of churches professedly unitarian. . . . We are, as it were, laying gunpowder, grain by grain, under the old building of error and superstition, which a single spark may hereafter inflame, so as to produce an instantaneous explosion; in consequence of which that edifice, the erection of which has been the work of ages, may be overturned in a moment, and so effectually as that the same foundation can never be built upon again. . . . And till things are properly ripe for such a revolution, it would be absurd to expect it, and in vain to attempt it.

Although Horsley had said that he would give no answer to anything further Priestley might say, he was in print again in the spring of 1786, inveighing against the decline of Calvinism among the English Dissenters. Priestley—this *emeritus* professor of Greek in the late academy at Warrington, as he was scathingly called—had been proved to be ignorant of his subject, Horsley remarked, and it followed that his conclusions, whatever they were, could only be right by accident.

But now an ominous new note was sounded. Horsley had found that neither Lindsey nor Priestley had signed the necessary declarations required by law to have their meeting-houses recognized, and so both were illegal conventicles. Lindsey hastened to rectify the oversight, with the help of Lee. Priestley took no notice. By making extracts from Priestley's writings from 1769 onwards, Horsley set out to show that they had a dangerous tendency and were subversive to the State. If Priestley ever attempted to carry out a fraction of what he appeared to threaten, it might become expedient for the magistrate to show his hand—but not yet.

Let us trust, therefore, for the present, as we securely may, to the trade of the good town of Birmingham, and to the wise connivance of the magistrate, (who watches, no doubt, while he deems it politic to wink,) to nip Dr Priestley's goodly projects in the bud; which nothing would be so likely to ripen to a dangerous effect, as constraint excessively or unseasonably used.

Priestley was not intimidated. His opponent being exhausted for the time being, he showed what he had been doing while the battle had been raging, and forthwith published a much more detailed study in four volumes, addressed directly to scholars, and entitled *An History of Early Opinions concerning Jesus Christ*. In May 1786 he told Lindsey that he was astonished at Horsley's obstinacy and blindness about the tenets of the early fathers, and that he would write a reply to his last pamphlet and have it ready in case it was called for. He thought the clergy were now ashamed of the treatment given to his book, and it seemed that Horsley's efforts had not given them the support they had hoped for—'nobody feels for them'. For much of this period he had been suffering from gall-stones but, surprisingly, by July all the symptoms had gone.

His new work, dated May 1786, was dedicated to Mrs Rayner. He hoped that it would be studied especially by those best qualified to demolish his arguments if they were incorrect.

On no former occasion have I declined, but on the contrary I have rather courted, and provoked, opposition, because I am sensible it is the only method of discovering truth; and I am far from wishing that this work may escape the most rigorous examination.

Horsley had said sarcastically: 'The conviction of the ortho-dox Trinitarian, that his philosophy is Plato's and his creed St John's, will alleviate the mortification he might otherwise feel in differing from Dr. Priestley.' The challenge of the new book consisted largely in the account it contained of the rise and progress of the doctrine of the Trinity, 'which sprung from the absurdity and mystery of Platonism'.

But, so a bishop told Priestley, no member of the Anglican clergy was equipped to undertake a public discussion of his work. They were in particular difficulties as regards the fourth volume, which contained an original and penetrating article headed 'Maxims of Historical Criticism', maxims which he himself had applied and which, in the main, could not be controverted. This, indeed, has by some been regarded as his most important contribution in the theological field. Mathe-maticians reason in an exact and rigorous manner; literary critics have laid down what they call canons of criticism; similarly, historians should know what were legitimate, and what unsound, methods of approach.

The work, nevertheless, received plenty of adverse comment, but much of it resembled the remarks of 'Philochristos' in *The Socinian Champion*:

> His list of sects in days of yore,
> And their sage dreams (price *one pound four*),
> Shall vanquish all the Trinitarians,
> And quite annihilate the Arians.

Lord Chancellor Thurlow, saying that those who defended the church should be supported by the church, made Horsley a prebendary of Gloucester, and in 1788 he became Bishop of St David's. It was already being mooted that the King had played a part in these events. On 1 March that year Lindsey wrote to a friend:

Bishop Hurd and the Chancellor, to gratify a great personage, as it is said, who is not very fond of Dissenters, and least of all of Dr. Priestley, are the promoters of Dr. Horsley to a bishopric; a promotion, however, which I am told, is very displeasing to many upon the bench.

But the noise of the controversy did not die down. At the end of the century Coleridge thought of reviewing the whole episode, and in 1810–12 two champions of the next generation joined the fray—Thomas Belsham for the Unitarians and Heneage Horsley for the Church. But it was then too late. Many people now allowed that there was some justice in Belsham's remark that both of the original contestants had retired content— Priestley with his victory, and Horsley with his mitre. Unitarianism was legalized in July 1813, a Bill for this purpose having been introduced by William Smith, who had been a staunch supporter of the Dissenters throughout the whole period. It was perhaps more than coincidence that at the same time the subject was being discussed by two former Presidents of the U.S.A.—Jefferson and Adams. Jefferson said that Priestley's *Early Opinions* had never been answered; he had read the book over and over again: and on it he based his faith.

The Corporation and Test Acts

On 28 March 1787 a motion was brought before Parliament for the repeal of the Corporation and Test Acts of 1661 and 1673, respectively, which effectively debarred Dissenters from holding civil, military, or naval appointments. Henry Beaufoy, F.R.S., the Member for Yarmouth, was chosen to present the case for the Dissenters. Beaufoy was a former Warrington student whose oration on 'the effects of civilization on the real improvement and happiness of mankind, in answer to Rousseau' had been published in 1768. He was ably supported by Charles James Fox. Pitt and North opposed the motion, and it was defeated by 176 votes to 98. Priestley listened to all the speeches; he respected the forthright stand adopted by North, but was offended by Pitt's evasiveness. He thereupon wrote and published a letter to Pitt, the tone of which displeased many Dissenters, for he told the young prime minister his business in a way he was never likely to forget—and never forgave.

Pitt had made much of the point that if the Dissenters were allowed this measure of relief, they would ask for more. Priestley agreed; and he proceeded to enumerate some of the things which they—or a more enlightened posterity—would probably demand.

But to quiet [the government's] apprehensions from the dangerous attempts of such furious sectaries as myself and my friends, and the terror which they have conceived from our gunpowder plots, &c. I shall inform them that the means we propose to employ are not *force*, but *persuasion*.

His gunpowder, on which Sir William Dolben had descanted in the House, was *arguments*.

First of all, he said, it should be legal for a man to declare and defend his religious principles, whatever they were, without fear of losing property or liberty. The law that made it blasphemy to impugn the doctrine of the Trinity should be repealed, together with all other penal laws in matters of religion. These were necessaries of life, he said, whereas the Corporation and Test Acts dealt only with the holding of offices, which were mere superfluities. Also, Dissenters should be free to celebrate marriage in their own places of worship.

But this was by no means all. The establishment should be confined to Christianity, certainly, but no serious Christian should be excluded from the Church. Pitt said this would lead to confusion, some believing one thing and some another. This was the position already, answered Priestley. Subscription at the universities should be abolished, for it had failed in its purpose—to keep Dissenters in ignorance. They had been forced to provide their own education at their own expense, instead of the State's ,and, being unfettered by subscription, their curriculum was more liberal. 'If it is so necessary for the clergy to believe those doctrines, let the subscription be confined to them.' To give so many of the clergy seats in the House of Lords debased their proper character. Dissenters should not be forced to contribute to the maintenance of the State Church; eventually the Church would be supported, not by tithes or any compulsion at all, but by 'the voluntary attachment of its friends', who would understand and value it.

But he would deprecate any violent changes. 'Any thing of this kind would counteract and defeat all my purposes. Every desirable step in the whole progress will be effected by the operation of *reason* alone, aided by *free enquiry*.' These, he said, were the thoughts of a man who had done everything in his power to add to his country's reputation, without seeking its emoluments.

Finally, he reminded Pitt that the people had been led by him to expect a reform in parliamentary representation, but as yet they had seen no signs of it.

There was an immediate reaction to this from some of the clergy. Any further relaxation, said one, was absolutely impracticable. If the Church was supported by voluntary attachment only, everyone would have the right publicly to teach whatever doctrines he thought fit and to contribute to the support of that religion, and that only, which he preferred. What would happen? Tumults, civil wars, all the horrors of the previous century. Such an experiment had never been tried before, except in America, where it was extremely hazardous, and likely to end in disaster.

Despite their disappointment, the Dissenters again pressed for the repeal of the Corporation and Test Acts in 1789, and Beaufoy and Fox again stated their claims on 8 May. On that occasion the motion was lost by 122 votes to 102. If few converts to their cause had been gained, the number of those who had decided not to vote against the motion had increased, and this raised hopes that a third application would be successful.

In the meantime Priestley had not been inactive. In 1788 he published a powerful sermon against the slave trade, and this did much to mollify his opponents among the more orthodox Dissenters. He also produced a second edition of his *Observations On Education*, together with his Warrington *Lectures on History and General Policy*, in response to a demand from the academies and certain colleges in America. In November 1789 he outlined the conduct to be observed by Dissenters in connection with a third application to Parliament, and reiterated in a calmly reasoned manner the rights that Dissenters should claim in the future. His arguments, said the reviewers, were unanswerable. Lindsey said that both friend and foe spoke most favourably of this pamphlet. 'I know not the man save himself, who could at once, at one sitting, with so much ease and perspicuity put together so much excellent sense upon the subject.'

In preparation for the third application for the repeal, numerous meetings of Dissenters were called throughout the country in December. Soon, however, it was clear that the Church had become alarmed and that opposition was being organized against them, especially in such towns as Leeds, Manchester, and Birmingham, places where Priestley himself had many friends and a strong following. In Birmingham the atmosphere became somewhat strained. On 3 January 1790 George Croft entered Spencer Madan's pulpit in St Philip's Church in order to defend the Test Laws. Justice and prudence, he said, demanded that the Church exert its utmost endeavours to exclude Dissenters from offices of trust and dignity. It would be fatal, he argued, if the legislature should declare all opinions innocent, and only on this principle could the Dissenters' demands be met.

Meetings of the clergy and other interested parties were called throughout the country early in February 1790. Some detected a sinister note about the Warwick County meeting of the 'principal noblemen, gentlemen and clergy' on 2 February. For one thing it suggested a solidarity among the leaders of the County which probably did not exist. Russell pointed out to the local Member of Parliament, Sir Robert Lawley, that it was altogether unrepresentative. Secondly, the purpose of the meeting was to consider 'proper measures for the defence of the constitution', scarcely a matter for a local meeting. And thirdly, the Earl of Aylesford had taken the chair and was thanked 'for the zeal he has shewn in support of the constitution, in church and state'.

On 14 February, Spencer Madan himself preached from the text: 'Put them in mind to be subject to principalities and powers, to obey magistrates. . . .' He was clearly treading in Horsley's footsteps. Several of his thoughts were Horsley's, and a pamphleteer asked him if he also was doing this for riches, power, honours, and ease. His quotations from Priestley's writings had been 'prostituted for political purposes', he was told. His aim appeared to be to destroy Priestley's good name in the town.

Towards the end of February Priestley wrote to Lindsey that party spirit was rising as the day set apart for the debate, 2 March, drew near.

Mr Russell says measures are taken to ring the bells, and illuminate the town on the expected event of Tuesday next, and in that case we apprehend the mob will be instigated to do mischief. We think to apply to Mr Garbett, Mr Boulton and a few others to prevent it.

On 1 March, when it was too late for any effective counter-measures to be taken, Members of Parliament received a printed series of extracts from Priestley's latest writings, arranged in such a way as to suggest imminent danger from a literal gun-powder plot, and this provided a clue as to the line the opposition would take. It was thus necessary for Fox, who had been chosen to propose the motion for the repeal, to deal with this misrepresentation.

Too much stress was being given to the opinions of a few individual Dissenters, he said. But even Priestley's declared opposition to the Church was no proof of a design to subvert the Ecclesiastical Constitution. He reminded the House that not many years before Pitt himself had expressed his absolute dis-satisfaction with the composition of the Commons and had stated that he would exert his powers to the utmost to remove anomalies and abuses in the system of representation: but he had done nothing about it. Surely, with such a supreme example of the trifling effect that opinions might have on practice, Priestley could be allowed to ascend even to the first rank in the Church without any danger to the religious constitution of the country. The Duke of Richmond once brought a Bill and argued that everyone over the age of 18 should be given a vote. Despite such revolutionary ideas, the Duke had been permitted to preside as head of the Board of Ordnance. Thus the holding of opinions, in itself, could not justify debarment from the holding of offices. If the Duke was not criminal, why was Priestley? Was the Church Establishment of more importance to the constitution than the representation of the people?

Some of the steps being taken by Priestley's antagonists, on the other hand, were quite unwarrantable, Fox said. Horsley

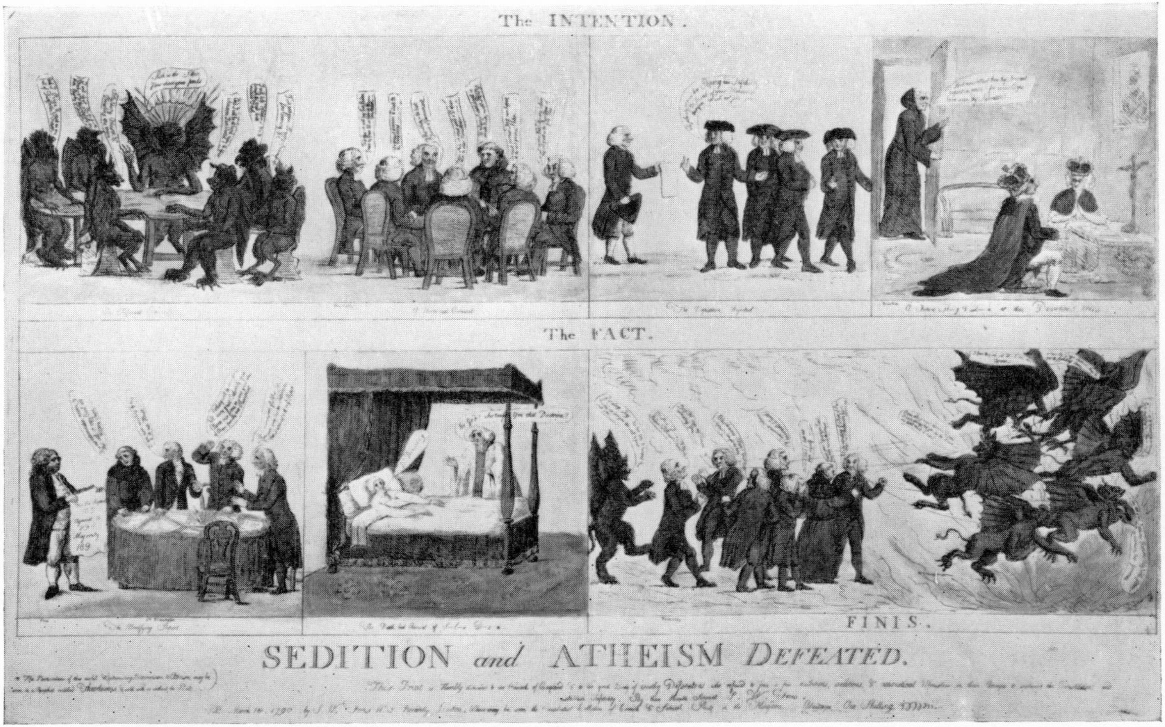

The INTENTION.

The FACT.

FINIS.

SEDITION and ATHEISM DEFEATED.

Plate 15 A cartoon published in March 1790, after the defeat of the motion for the Repeal of the Test Act. This print, which was occasioned by a defamatory pamphlet entitled *Theodosius*, shows Priestley and his brother Dissenters, with Fox, Stanhope and others (*bottom left*) accused and convicted of sedition and atheism. Other incidents, such as the death-bed 'confession' of Silas Deane, were being discussed in the press. (*British Museum*)

Plate 16 William Priestley being introduced by M. Français to the National Assembly in Paris. Priestley first heard of this through the newspapers. Note the jar of phlogiston from Hackney College. (*British Museum*)

had been guilty of breach of privilege, when, at a recent election, he had haughtily dictated who should, and who should not, be returned to Parliament. He had said that he should consider each of his clergy who refused to vote for Sir William Mansell as faithless to his sacred trust and criminally remiss in the execution of his duties. He could hardly have thought of a better way to make the Dissenters declared enemies of the Church.

Richard Price, too, had given offence by his sermon *On the Love of Our Country*, preached in November 1789 on the anniversary of the Revolution of 1688. He had rejoiced over the establishment of a new régime in America, and shared the delight of many with the revolution then taking place in France. But, said Fox, it was clear that he spoke as a citizen of the world glorying in the freedom and happiness of the human race. Price's only mistake was his choice of time and place for his remarks, said Fox—they would have been better as a speech in a House of Parliament.

But it was Burke, formerly a friend of Priestley and the Dissenters, who most effectively handled the misleading evidence with which he had been supplied. He mentioned the printed catechisms of Robinson and Palmer (converts of Priestley and Lindsey) to suggest that young Dissenters were being taught to abjure Church and King. The very being of the Church was in danger, for this might lead to the same fate that had overtaken the established church in France. At a Dissenters' meeting at Bolton [1]—he could have mentioned many others, too—it transpired that the repeal of the Test Laws was regarded merely as a preliminary to the abolition of tithes and other measures. He then produced Priestley's gunpowder letter, which would blow up the Church if the danger was not averted by its friends. It was a serious indication of his determination 'to proceed, step by step, till the whole of the Church Establishment was levelled to its foundations'. He then read an extract from Price's sermon.

Pitt said little, but took advantage of the opportunity to criticize both Horsley and Priestley. Both were to blame for going beyond their province. The clergy should not blend affairs

[1] Apparently Warrington was intended.

of state with sacred matters, for it could lead only to discord; they should be concerned solely with the advancement of piety, morality, and truth.

Other speakers for the repeal included Beaufoy, Sir Henry Hoghton (for some years President of the Warrington Academy), and William Smith, who attempted to answer Burke's arguments in some detail. But Burke, having said that he would not vote against the motion, had left the House. There seemed no point in continuing the debate, and the motion was heavily defeated by 294 votes to 105. Fox had begun to speak at half past four in the afternoon, but the House did not rise until nearly three o'clock on the Wednesday morning.

The Rising Storm

The 'Church and King' party had finally demonstrated its power, but Priestley and his friends smarted under a sense of injustice. At Manchester abuse of the Dissenters was the order of the day. At Birmingham, however, the clergy were moderate. On the day the news arrived, bells began to ring at all the churches, but they soon stopped. At Warwick they rang all day. 'The church people in general think that we shall now be quiet, and give them no trouble a long time,' Priestley wrote. 'When they find the contrary, they will be much chagrined.'

Priestley had answered the attack delivered by Madan from the pulpit of St Philip's Church in two sets of *Familiar Letters* to the inhabitants of Birmingham. Madan was known to have prepared a reply, which was due to be published on a Thursday towards the end of March. Priestley now decided to take the initiative, and arranged for a third set of *Familiar Letters* to be released to the booksellers on the same day. He later told Lindsey that Madan's letter had proved to be both 'peevish and malignant'. He produced a fourth set of letters in the first week of April, when he heard that he was being threatened with the spiritual court. On 6 April, however, he wrote: 'The clergy are exasperated to the greatest degree, but I have just heard that, after a solemn consultation they have dropped their scheme.' But he made no attempt to placate them. Indeed, seeing that his opponents were losing their tempers, he prepared a final part of his *Letters*, in which he set out to show the unhappy state of affairs in the Church of England itself.

The rest of April 1790 he spent in London, returning early in May. He had been in consultation with Fox, whom he tried to interest in Unitarianism. Their names were linked in the political prints, especially those of Sayers, which Fox feared but which were a source of merriment in the Priestley household. Their favourites were one in which Lindsey and Priestley, in the same pulpit, were shown haranguing a number of public figures of the day (Plate 14), and another in which they were depicted being jostled by demons on their way to hell (Plate 15). Priestley's daughter, Sally, made a collection of them.

Not only the prints revelled in this new topic for mockery and satire. A fantastic number of miscellaneous publications, from serious attacks by bishops to the scurrilous efforts of petty versifiers, began to clutter the bookshops. This had been going on for some time, but it was intensified after Priestley's public exchanges with Madan and Burn. At the same time threats began to be expressed more openly. Madan, for example, had told an anecdote in a suggestive manner. Chatham, when a young man, had said to Sir Robert Walpole: 'when an old hound misleads the pack, the only way of treating him, is, to *hang him at once*'. Madan, himself a young man, had been told by Priestley to leave the discussion of serious matters to those more experienced. It was clear that Madan, Horsley, and Burn wished to discredit Priestley so that people would not read his books. 'And that is certainly the shortest way with me, and the most effectual, short of *hanging me up*, and collecting and burning all my publications,' Priestley replied.

Soon a lower note was struck in some *Very Familiar Letters* addressed to Priestley by one who signed himself John Nott, button burnisher.

If you ben't melancholy made, as I guess you be, what makes you rave so much about *gunpowder*. You never write but you tell us church people, that you're *laying it grain by grain under the churches* and mean to blow 'em up all together very soon. . . . Now, prithee Mr. Priestley, how would you like it yourself, if they were to send you word that they had laid trains of gunpowder under your house or meeting-house?

What of Priestley's loyalty? He had written that 'another king is arisen that knoweth not Joseph'. To which Nott replied: 'Belike there has, master Joseph, but what of that? . . . I wonder you ben't ashamed master Priestley to throw this in the king's teeth; as if as how he ought to know every body.' After more play with words, he added: 'Who knows but we may give you a *shove* yet, and then the King can't help knowing that there is such a man as Joseph Priestley!' The common folk of Birmingham, he said, were beginning to regret that he had ever come to live among them—'to throw us into hot water, and kick up such a dust as you have done'.

Though this booklet was the subject of some *Very Familiar Letters to Mr. John Nott*, from Alexander Armstrong, whip-maker, and Abel Sharp, spur-maker, some damage was inevitable, particularly as several editions of it were printed. But there were not many who, like Gregory Dominic, tried to be fair and to say that, to the ordinary man, all this business was rather tiresome:

> Mechanics, now, have caught the scribbling hint;
> And love, like Priestley, to appear in print . . .
>
> Against thee, Priestley! their abuses fly;
> 'Gainst thee they raise the partial *hue and cry*!
> Exaggerate whatever is impure;
> And, thy bright virtues, blindly do obscure:
> And give to *weakness*, a conspicuous place.
> Thy share of persecution hast thou got:
> For persecution is the good man's lot . . .

Yet in these heated discussions Priestley had not been faultless:

> Too proud he is to own he ever err'd:
> He, woman-like, will have the final word;
> And knows not where to end, when once begun;
> But, spite of self-conviction, still writes on.

This mention of weakness seems to have been a reference to an incident that had occurred in January 1790, and had made Priestley wonder seriously about his physical security. He was confined to his home for several weeks with extreme hoarseness, following a period when he had been troubled by a return of his stammer. At this time, between two and three o'clock on a Sunday morning, three men attempted to break in. A pistol was fired at a maid who opened a window to see the cause of the disturbance. The way this incident was retailed by John Nott could only have given more pain. He wrote:

> . . . don't you remember what a parlous taking you was in one Saturday, when one of our Birmingham gunners shot at a flight of sparrows in your garden thinking no harm. Why you set a ringing your great bell and whirling your rattle and so you rais'd the neighbourhood; and thof all your Presbyterian friends at Foullake [1] (and you've a good many there) huddled about you with their smelling-bottles and drops, alack, they cou'dn't put spirits enough into you to carry you to meeting to do your duty o' Sunday. So if the truth was known, mayhap, you're as much afeard of a flash in the pan as other folks.

A further difficulty arose from the continual prodding of his republican-minded friends to go beyond the limits of reason and argument which he had laid down. One of the main centres of this restlessness was the neighbourhood of Hackney, the home ground of Richard Price, the Vaughans, and the brothers William and John Hurford Stone, as well as a recently founded academy, New College. Several of these, particularly the Stones and some of the students, were loud in their praise of the French revolution and longed to see some action in England, too. There was a heated reaction to the rejection of Fox's motion on 2 March 1790, and this became more intense on 4 March, when Henry Floyd's motion for improving parliamentary representation was dismissed out of hand, Floyd being told that the subject was dead and that it should be postponed for a century. William Stone forthwith called upon Priestley to make an address to the nation. This might well have led to civil disturbances, and was opposed to Priestley's avowed principles. He immediately replied that he would do no such thing.

There were other troubles. In Birmingham, the clergy began once again to try to influence the policy of the library, now well established. In particular, they tried to prevent controversial writings on theology coming into the subscribers' hands. The

---

[1] An earlier name for the Fair Hill area.

argument proceeded for several months and came to a head at a meeting on 22 December 1790. The Rector had spent some time canvassing votes for the occasion and was the chief speaker for the suggestion. Russell spoke against it. The proposal was rejected by two-thirds of those present, although the clergy had exerted themselves to obtain support and came in full strength. Priestley told Lindsey that 'the high church party is thoroughly humbled and we triumphant'. But Priestley's pleasure was not widely shared for long; as Hutton detected, a new phase of the quarrel had begun.

To the country as a whole the progress of the revolution in France was of paramount interest. The rift between Fox and Burke during the debate on 2 March became a complete break by the early summer of 1791, and this proved to be a turning-point in English political history; many have seen in it the birth of the Liberal party. Liberalism was a positive philosophy —a belief in the value of human personality, and a conviction that all human progress was due to the free exercise of man's powers. This in turn could only be secured by the free expression of opinions and by the removal of all unnecessary restraints on thought and action. The story of the Liberal party's struggles in the nineteenth century for political, civil, and religious liberty is now being seen increasingly by historians as a continuation of the battle in which Priestley himself was engaged as deeply as any individual of his generation.

On one point Burke was proved right. He took a gloomy view of the way the revolution in France was likely to develop, and he believed it to be his duty to warn against any similar trends in Great Britain. This he did in his *Reflections on the Revolution in France, and on the Proceedings in certain Societies in London relative to that Event*. As a superb literary achievement, 'the most magnificent political prophecy ever given to the world', it was received with great acclaim, and praised even by many of those against whom it was directed. But its main aim, to prevent any further tendency towards 'innovations' or relaxations to the Dissenters at that point in history, has been partly forgotten. Certainly he had his eye on the Hackney circle, among others.

The groups to which Burke referred in his title were the Society for Constitutional Information (founded in 1780) and the Revolution Society (supported largely by the more liberal Whigs who desired to commemorate the Glorious Revolution of 1688). It was to the latter that Price had preached 'On the Love of our Country'. Soon it became apparent that Burke's attack was being levelled against the leaders of these societies, such as Lord Stanhope, together with Price and Priestley. Speaking of the revolution in France, he said:

The wild *gas*, the fixed air, is plainly broke loose: but we ought to suspend our judgment until the first effervescence is a little subsided, till the liquor is cleared, and until we see something deeper than the agitation of a troubled and frothy surface.

He looked on Price's sermon as the public declaration of a man involved with literary caballers, intriguing philosophers, political theologians, and theological politicians. These men were wholly 'unacquainted with the world in which they are so fond of meddling, and inexperienced in all its affairs, on which they pronounce with so much confidence'. This was a common, though unfair allusion to the fact that the Dissenters were still prevented from attending the universities and holding civil offices. Burke then spoke of 'our new fanatics of popular arbitrary power' who regarded the will of the people as the sole lawful source of authority. And he concluded this section of his book with a thought which could only mean repression for those who wished to see changes introduced.

We are resolved to keep an established church, an established monarchy, an established aristocracy, and an established democracy, each in the degree it exists, and in no greater.

Though all who approved this sentiment were loud in their applause, it would be wrong to imagine that such views immediately swept the country. Some forty publications were issued against the book, and, like Priestley, many were deeply affected by what they regarded as a fall from grace of one they had formerly regarded as a brother. The book appeared in November 1790, and Priestley was among the first to reply with an outspoken pamphlet that reached its third edition by the middle of January 1791.

Burke, he said, had patronized the liberty of America, where there was no established church, and where civil offices could be held by men of all persuasions. But he then decried the revolution in France, although it was based on the same general principles as the American. And now he denied to his fellow countrymen the liberties he favoured for America.

Burke's attack on Price had been unjust. The friends of the revolution in France rejoiced in the good, the new access of freedom, but not the evil that accompanied it. Burke approved the English revolution of 1688, but now said there could be no further changes of any kind or degree. This, Priestley bluntly stated, quoting an Act of Queen Anne, amounted to high treason.

Far am I from wishing to bring you into any serious inconvenience by representing you as having offended against the laws of your country; but I wish it may serve as a hint, to pay more attention to the great principles of our constitution, as well as to the universal principles of government, and the *rights of men*, offensive as the term may be to you, for the future.

Burke had been incensed by the Revolution Society's having sent a congratulatory message to the National Assembly in Paris; but that did not excuse him for his damaging reference to it as the society for revolutions.

To Priestley, the aims of such revolutions as those of America and France should be, first, government for the general good, allowing all men the enjoyment of as many of their natural rights as possible, and no more interference in religion than in philosophy or medicine. Governments eventually could be expected to confine their attention to civil matters. This in turn should lead to the extinction of all national prejudices, and the establishment of universal peace and good will among the nations. He then attempted to give a glimpse of what his aspirations might mean for the future.

The very idea of *distant possessions* will be even ridiculed . . . only those divisions of men, and of territory, will take place, which the common convenience requires, and not such as the mad and insatiable ambition of princes demands. No part of America, Africa, or Asia, will be held in subjection to any part of Europe, and all the intercourse that will be kept up among them, will be for their mutual advantage.

If at any time there was a surplus of public money, it should be spent on public works, not on the enormous expenses of governments and wars.

The expence of the late American war only would have converted all the waste grounds of this country into gardens. What canals, bridges, and noble roads, &c. &c. would it not have made for us? If the pride of nations must be gratified, let it be spent in such things as these. . . .

Eventually the peoples of the world would adopt any method of settling their differences rather than go to war, for 'the empire of reason will ever be the reign of peace'.

This is a state of things which good sense, and the prevailing spirit of commerce, aided by christianity, and true philosophy, cannot fail to effect in time. . . .
In this new condition of the world, there may still be kings, but they will be no longer sovereigns, or supreme lords. There will be magistrates, appointed and paid for the conservation of order, but they will only be considered as the first servants of the people, and accountable to them. Standing armies, those instruments of tyranny, will be unknown, though the people may be trained to the use of arms, for the purpose of repelling the invasion of Barbarians. For no other description of men will have recourse to war, or think of disturbing the repose of others; and till they become civilized, as in the natural progress of things they necessarily must, they will be sufficiently overawed by the superior power of nations that are so.

All this speculation, which exhilarated him, led to his chief contention that it would be better to relax now and introduce measures that would prove for the ultimate benefit of the country, than to force a situation that might come to resemble that in France. Such a crisis would be even more serious for this country, since it was more dependent on its manufactures and commerce and had fewer internal resources.

If this be a dream, it is, however, a pleasing one, and has nothing in it malignant, or unfriendly to any. All that I look to promises no exclusive advantage to myself, or my friends; but an equal field for every generous exertion to all, and it makes the great object of all our exertions to be the public good.

But relaxation of the laws, or a state bordering on revolution, were only two of the possibilities. Priestley did not seem to think that a third would be seriously entertained—forceful repression

Chapter 13

The Horrors of 'Ninety-One

IT was partly coincidence that the three men Burke chiefly wrote against—Stanhope, Price, and Priestley—were 'innovators' in science as well as in politics. But at that time few people of public spirit, whatever their pursuits, could keep themselves aloof from the political and religious questions that were rocking the foundations of society.

Charles Stanhope, the third earl, was more than the eccentric nobleman that some have painted him, for he was eminent both as an experimenter and an inventor. He made improvements in building materials, and in the construction of houses to reduce the likelihood of fire. He was a pioneer in the design of calculating machines, for both multiplication and division. While Wilkinson was thinking of using iron for bridges and boats, Stanhope was trying to apply the steam-engine to navigation. While Boulton was working on improved coinage, Stanhope published the results of an inquiry into means of preventing fraudulent practices, including a suggestion for milling gold coins. In 1777 Priestley dedicated his third volume of experiments to Stanhope's father, Philip, the second earl, saying that he was 'distinguished among the English nobility, as a lover of science, and a steady friend of the liberties of his country, and those of mankind'. Charles shared all his father's interests and enthusiasms, and these words of Priestley were equally applicable to him.

After July 1789 many began to wonder what changes these somewhat radical philosophers might try to bring about in their own country. In November that year, when various societies were sending congratulatory messages to the French National Assembly, such thoughts found open expression. Thus George

Selwyn, wit and politician, writing to Lady Carlisle, who was then holidaying abroad, reported: [1]

> We are at peace at home, I thank God, *pour le moment*. I hope that it will continue, and that no Lord Stanhope, or a Dr. Priestley, will think a change of government would make us happier.

This was a year before the publication of Burke's *Reflections*. That Priestley should have been regarded in such a light appears the more remarkable when it is remembered that a very large number of associations and societies existed in many parts of the country for the avowed object of securing the introduction of reforms. The evidence all confirms the statement of Priestley himself that he belonged to no party, to no political association, and to no society—other than a religious one. With some of these, however, even Burke and Pitt had dealings.

In 1782 the Yorkshire Association had been in correspondence with Samuel Vaughan, who assisted Price, Jebb, and others to work out a plan for parliamentary reform. This was adopted by the Yorkshire Committee, and Pitt afterwards used it as the basis of a motion debated by Parliament in April 1785. In short, it proposed that 36 'rotten' boroughs should be disenfranchised in order to introduce a more equitable representation of the counties and of the metropolis, and four other boroughs disenfranchised in favour of the largest manufacturing towns still unrepresented, namely, Birmingham, Manchester, Sheffield, and Leeds.

Christopher Wyvill, chairman of the Yorkshire Committee, wrote to prominent citizens in these towns in January 1785, hoping to persuade them to raise petitions in support of the plan. But Wyvill, contrary to his expectations, found no zeal whatever for the idea. He concluded that this indicated a lack of support for reform among members of the established Church in these towns. However, at this time the numbers of Churchmen and Dissenters in the large manufacturing centres were almost equal, and there was no desire on the part of the employers to cause any disturbance. Wyvill met with no response from Boulton, or from Samuel Garbett, who was chairman of

[1] Hist. MSS. Comm., Rep. 15, App. VI, 677.

Birmingham's Commercial Committee at a time when Russell, Boulton, and Priestley's neighbour, George Humphrys, were among its members. Soon afterwards Russell informed Wyvill that no petition was to be expected from Birmingham; according to Priestley, the reason for this was merely indifference.

The upshot was unfortunate for the friends of reform. When Pitt presented the motion, Lord North asked that the Clerk of the House should read the petitions from Birmingham and Manchester, knowing that there were none. From that moment the Bill was doomed. Thus the chances of a national movement beginning in a town like Birmingham at that time must have been slight, and this fact must surely have been known to the Government.

Though the London Society for Constitutional Information held its first meeting in 1780, it was not until the French revolution had got under way that such societies were formed in the large manufacturing towns. The first of these, the Manchester Constitutional Society, was instituted in October 1790. Prominent among this group was Thomas Cooper, a chemist friend of Priestley, and one who also had the misfortune to be distrusted by Burke. An informer had provided Burke with misleading information about the part Cooper played as chairman of a Dissenters' meeting at Warrington, and he had used this in the House of Commons on 2 March. Cooper subsequently published an indignant denial. Priestley, with the help of Kirwan, Watt, and others, had tried to secure Cooper's election to the Royal Society, but here, too, he met with opposition. The King's two librarians and many church dignitaries had found it necessary to attend the meeting, and they managed to raise a straight majority of votes against him, when one-third would have been sufficient for their purpose. The fact that one of the Manchester Constitutional Society's chief functions was to dine annually on 14 July to celebrate the freedom of France did not encourage the Government to look on it with favour, and Burke's *Reflections*, which appeared a month after the Society's formation, cast doubt on the activities of all such societies.

During this time Priestley was having the utmost difficulty in finding positions for his sons Joseph and William, Harry being still at school with Estlin at Bristol. He had tried many

possibilities for Joseph, but time and again he met an unfavour-
able response. Eventually, in February 1791, a merchant at
Manchester agreed to take him as a clerk, with a view later on
to a partnership. This was a great relief, though it proved to be
only temporary. William, who had been in Paris in the early
days of the revolution, had settled for a time with a family at
Frankfort, but had returned to Birmingham in 1790. A highly
strung youth, and not easily disciplined, he failed to obtain an
appointment with Wilkinson. By December it had been agreed
that he should be articled to Russell for three years with a view
to going on afterwards to America. But, Priestley was forced to
admit, his 'temper and high spirits' were hardly suited to trade.

By the end of February 1791 the country was in a most
unsettled state. Priestley was hearing much about the offence
his letters to Burke had given in high quarters. He had also
learnt that Shelburne (now Lord Lansdowne) had written to
Garbett saying that Pitt was determined to force a war with
France; but they were relieved to learn in early March that the
threat of war had receded.

Priestley was now preparing for his annual April visit to
London, when he normally relieved Price from his preaching
duties. This year, however, he had more reasons than usual for
being anxious to get away. Price had been seriously ill, though
for the moment he was thought to be out of danger. Priestley
had also undertaken to give the anniversary discourse to the
friends of the New College, Hackney, which, starting in bad
circumstances without a building of its own, had not progressed
as well as had been hoped. There was some truth in what
Coleridge afterwards said of it to Estlin: 'the tutors, the *whole*
plan of education, the place itself, were all wrong'. Freedom of
thought for the young, without adequate discipline, was in those
unsettled times liable to give rise to more harm than good, at
least, from the public's point of view. Thus some of the students
professed to have adopted deism as their creed, and were
republican in politics.

To Burke the New College, where Price was a tutor, was a
'hot-bed of sedition'. No doubt he remembered that students
from Hackney had been present in Westminster Hall during his
presentation of the case against Warren Hastings in 1788-9,

and had flocked to the gallery of the House of Commons on the night of 2 March 1790. Several of them showed sympathy towards the views of Thomas Paine, whose answer to Burke's *Reflections* was avidly read in February 1791. Priestley thought highly of this first part of Paine's *The Rights of Man*, the boldest publication he had ever seen on the subject.

On 11 April he left for London, having arranged to stay there for three weeks, and to preach for Price on 1 May. But on 19 April Price died, and Priestley was one of the six ministers who a week later carried him to his grave in Bunhill Fields. On 1 May Priestley preached at Hackney, as arranged, but his sermon took the form of a memorial address for the friend he had known for thirty years. They had disagreed on many things, but both had clung firmly to the belief that 'virtuous men shall meet after death in a state of happiness'. Mrs Barbauld was present on the occasion, and remarked on the absence of sadness.[1] 'Dr. Priestley parts with his intimate friend with all the cheerfulness which an assured hope of meeting him soon again could give, and at once dries the tear he excites.'

Already on 27 April he had spoken to the supporters of the New College on *The proper Objects of Education in the present State of the World*. His address, which contained the core of his whole philosophy, rivalled Paine's in boldness, and it was thought in official circles that he should be taken to account for it. When the address was published, it became clear that he offered no comfort to the Church, and still less to the Government—and he was prepared for anything either or both could do to him.

The new light bursting out on all sides, he said, showed that at last mankind was beginning to understand the meaning of the civil rights of men and the purpose of civil government.

While so favourable a wind is abroad, let every young mind expand itself, catch the rising gale, and partake of the glorious enthusiasm; the great objects of which are the flourishing state of science, arts, manufactures, and commerce, the extinction of wars, with the calamities incident to mankind from them, the abolishing of all useless distinctions, which were the offspring of a barbarous age, (producing an absurd haughtiness in some, and a base servility in others) and a general release from all such taxes, and burdens of

[1] Lucy Aikin, *The Works of Anna Laetitia Barbauld*, London, 1825, ii, 84.

every kind, as the public good does not require. In short, to make government as beneficial, and as little expensive and burdensome, as possible.

In addition to this, he said, the world required to be 're-christianized'. The two main forces of the day were a spurious Christianity on the one hand, and infidelity on the other. And so the modern reformers were in a similar position to that of the apostles. The Church could be expected to look more and more to its own safety, and so those who introduced reforms should expect every kind of abuse and persecution that the spirit of the age was capable of producing.

If even burning alive was a sight that the country would now bear, there exists a spirit which would inflict that horrid punishment, and with as much cool indifference or savage exultation, as in any preceding age of the world. But youth should be so trained up, as, without fear, to look for every species of ill usage in a good cause. Such is the force of truth, especially when urged by men who themselves feel the force of it, and who respect nothing but truth, that it will now, as formerly, prevail over all opposition. The world may bear down particular *men*, but they cannot bear down a *good cause*; and in the steady support of it such men will not much regard what is done to themselves.

Early in May, Priestley returned to Birmingham. Soon all eyes were again turned to France. Since the previous October, Louis XVI and Marie Antoinette had been virtually prisoners in the Tuileries, though Louis remained the nominal head of the state. To the 'Church and King' party in England such a situation was intolerable, and the news of the Royal family's escape from Paris in June was a matter for jubilation. For Priestley and the friends of the revolution it was a time of great anxiety. The flight of the king was halted at Varennes on 22 June, and he was taken back to Paris and detained under somewhat stricter surveillance.

Commenting on these events to Lindsey, Priestley said: 'our joy on his capture, cannot be described'. These few simple words reveal the intensity of feeling with which developments in France were being watched. Again there was a sharp division of opinion. 'The high party would have had the country

[France] involved in civil war for the imaginary rights of one man.' He went on to say that in spite of 'all we can write, or do, an attachment to high maxims of government gains ground here, and the love of liberty is on the decline. Such is the influence of the Court.'

For once Priestley had made no arrangements to go away for the summer, and he thanked God for the good state of his health, which made an excursion unnecessary. His wife wished to remain near at hand, as Sally, who had married William Finch and lived at the Heath Forge, Dudley, was expecting a child near the end of August. After that, they proposed to go to John Wilkinson's country house at Castle Head.

In view of the state of political feeling in Birmingham, Priestley's friends in London must have been surprised to read, in his letter of 29 June: 'We are forming a Constitutional Society here similar to that in Manchester.' For the moment they were proposing to hold two annual dinners, the first on 14 July.

More than eighty well-known people agreed to attend the dinner, and Capt. James Keir, a member of the Church of England, accepted the office of chairman. The first advertisement was dated 7 July, from the Hotel, and announced that dinner would be on the table at 3 p.m. precisely on 14 July.

Any Friend to Freedom, disposed to join the intended temperate festivity, is desired to leave his name at the bar of the Hotel, where tickets may be had at Five Shillings each, including a bottle of wine; but no person will be admitted without one.

On the second appearance of the advertisement, in the *Birmingham Gazette*, another notice accompanied it, as follows:

On Friday next will be published, price One Halfpenny,
An authentic list of all those who dine at the Hotel, Temple Row, Birmingham, on Thursday the 14th instant, in commemoration of the French Revolution.

Vivant Rex et Regina.

At about the same time a few copies of a handbill were found under the tables at an inn, and in two factories. Where they had come from was a complete mystery, though they were afterwards believed to have emanated from Hackney. There may

14

have been some substance in this, as it was afterwards known that William Stone was in the Birmingham area at the time. The concluding paragraph of the handbill sufficiently shows its import.

But on the 14th of this month, prove to the political sychophants of the day, that You reverence the Olive Branch; that You *will* sacrifice to public Tranquility, till the Majority *shall* exclaim, *The Peace of Slavery is worse than the War of Freedom.* Of that moment let Tyrants beware.

Many agreed with Hutton's view of this leaflet and its unknown author: 'I have been tempted to question whether he meant any more than a squib to attract public attention; but it proved a dreadful one, which burnt our houses.' With what many observers regarded as suspicious alacrity, a further paper was circulated, pointing out that the seditious handbill distributed that morning made false statements about the Government. The new leaflet, written in a challenging vein, could scarcely have failed to provoke a strong response.

Whatever the *modern republicans* may imagine, or the *regicidal propounders of the rights of men* design, let us convince them there is enough of loyalty in the majority of the inhabitants of this country, to *support* and *defend* their King . . .

The magistrates, the High Bailiff, and nine other gentlemen offered a reward of 100 guineas on the morning of 14 July to anyone identifying either the writer, printer, publisher, or distributor of the first leaflet, though no objection appears to have been taken to the second. A similar reward was afterwards offered by the Dissenters, and again by the Government. These expressions of disapproval, however, were of little consequence, for they merely served to deflect attention from the second leaflet, which showed that some were only too ready to run to the support and defence of the King—even before any danger had arisen. At the same time the Constitutional Society (though they avoided calling themselves by this name) issued an announcement declaring their entire disapproval of all the handbills that had appeared, for they could 'only be intended to create distrust concerning the intention of the meeting, to disturb its harmony, and inflame the minds of the people'.

They vowed their firm attachment to the constitution, as vested in the three estates of King, Lords, and Commons. Then, referring to the purpose of the celebration, they added:

Surely no Free-born Englishman can refrain from exulting in this addition to the general mass of human happiness? It is the cause of Humanity! It is the Cause of the People!

At one time during the morning of 14 July it was decided to cancel the dinner, and a notice to that effect was being set up by a local printer; however Dadley, the landlord of the Hotel, persuaded them to carry on as arranged, but to leave reasonably early. As a further precaution Priestley, against whom feeling seemed to be mounting, was persuaded to stay at home. Several people gathered at the entrance to the Hotel before the diners arrived, and they hissed and hustled them as they went in. The dinner proceeded without interruption, nineteen toasts were drunk, and the party separated early, between 5 and 6 p.m., going out a few at a time. By about 8 p.m. a large and more riotous crowd had collected outside the building. Although two magistrates were present, and the mob was informed that the diners had left, they at last lost patience and proceeded to break the windows along the front of the tavern.

It was a calm, warm evening, and for much of the night the moon shone brightly. The crowd was in no mood to disperse, and, as if briefed beforehand, they moved off to the New Meeting. The gates and doors were soon opened, pews were demolished, wood, cushions, and the library from the vestry were brought out, and a fire was started in front of the building. Lighted fragments were then carried inside, and the whole was burnt to a shell.

In addition, the Old Meeting was attacked by a second party with crow-bars, bludgeons, and the like. Pulpit, pews, and galleries were torn down and burnt in the burying-ground. After this the building itself was set alight. Many other buildings in the vicinity were threatened by the fire, but eventually the water-engines were brought along, and the rioters allowed them to be used in protection of the adjoining buildings, but not of the Old Meeting. The danger only passed when the roof collapsed and the outer walls fell. It was later learned that the

keys to the building where the engines were kept had been
taken from the official custodian by order of the Vicar of
St Martin's, and that this had greatly delayed their arrival.
Detachments from both Meetings moved off and proceeded to
Fair Hill, rather more than a mile from the town.

Meanwhile Samuel Ryland got wind of their plan and drove
out to Fair Hill in his chaise; he found Priestley and his wife
unaware of what was happening and enjoying an evening game
of backgammon. With difficulty they were persuaded to go on
with Ryland to the Russells at Showell Green; William
Priestley, some other young people, and the servants were left
to protect the property. At about the same time a messenger
arrived at the Russells, saying that the mob intended to come
on there after destroying Priestley's house. The magistrates
could no longer be found, and nobody appeared to be trying to
stop them. Russell, despite his deafness, quickly understood the
position, called for his horse, and loaded his pocket-pistols. At
that point the Priestleys arrived.

They all tried to prevent Russell going out, but he insisted.
Mrs Priestley thereupon begged him to fetch a box of money
from her room, and her husband asked for the pocket-book he
had left lying on the table. Now they all walked up and down
the road outside the house in a state of apprehension, for they
could see the fires from the two meeting-houses and hear the
shouts of the advancing mob. But this, it transpired, was only a
detachment of twenty to thirty men, and Russell did not meet
them. He hastily got together some friends, and took them to
Priestley's house, leaving them there to help William Priestley
to remove as many manuscripts and books as possible, and take
them to what he considered a safe place nearby. (Unfortunately,
it seems that this cache was later discovered.) He then rode on
towards Birmingham.

Soon after this the first detachment arrived. Priestley's friends
spoke to them, gave them drink, and persuaded them to go
away. Russell had now gone as far as Digbeth, where he met
the main mob, which prevented his going any farther. Eventually he gave up the attempt and returned to Fair Hill. When
the mob came up he tried to reason with them and offer them
money. In reply they began to stone him. He thereupon rode up

to the house, told William Priestley to secure the building as well as he could, and rode back to Showell Green, which he had left some three hours earlier. It was now well after midnight, but having been warned that he also could expect a visit, he decided that they should all walk to the house of another friend, about half a mile away at Moseley Wake Green, having left a barrel of ale on the front lawn, and servants to guard the property. From their friend's house they could hear the shouts of the mob at Fair Hill, interspersed with the noise of battering against the walls, and a confusion of sounds due to the breaking of windows, shutters, furniture, banisters, and everything movable. At first the rioters overlooked the laboratory, as it was some little distance from the house, but eventually this also was broken into, and much of the contents destroyed. Perhaps it was here that they found the remnants of a fire, which for a time they had been unable to raise. The well-stocked cellar had been entered, and what could not be drunk was thrown on the floor. They then set fire to the house, and when day broke the fields around were strewn with prostrate figures, sleeping from fatigue and drunkenness. Russell returned to his family about 4 a.m. to say that all was now quiet, and that it appeared safe to return to Showell Green, as the mob would be unlikely to attempt anything further in daylight.

Of Priestley's deportment that night nothing but admiration was expressed by all who saw him. No account of those critical hours, however, has a more genuine ring than Martha Russell's, written soon afterwards.

Undaunted he heard the blows which were destroying the house and laboratory that contained all his valuable and rare apparatus and their effects, which it had been the business of his life to collect and use . . . he, tranquil and serene, walked up and down the road with a firm yet gentle pace that evinced his entire self-possession, and a complete self-satisfaction and consciousness which rendered him thus firm and resigned under the unjust and cruel persecution of his enemies. . . Not one hasty or impatient expression, not one look expressive of murmur or complaint, not one tear or sigh escaped him; resignation and a conscious innocence and virtue seemed to subdue all these feelings of humanity.

A room was hastily got ready for the Priestleys, and they had just prepared to rest when Russell came in with the news that the rioters were assembling again, and were swearing to find Priestley and take his life. The chaise was ordered, the Priestleys were forced to dress again, and Ryland took them by a side-road to Heath to stay for a while with their daughter. Here Mrs Priestley remained. As they were not discovered, Priestley did not leave until the Saturday afternoon, when he set out on horseback with a servant to go to Worcester (Ryland having left in advance to book a place in his own name in the London mail). When crossing a common between Heath and Bridg-north, however, they lost their way. Darkness fell, and they wandered about all night, getting only as far as Kidderminster by the morning. Ryland, apparently sensing trouble, had returned to Kidderminster, where he met Priestley, and accompanied him to Worcester. They were just in time to catch the mail, and there they parted. Priestley travelled all night, arriving in London early on the Monday morning. He went straight to Lindsey.

The Rev. W. Jesse, of West Bromwich, who went into Birmingham on the Saturday, sent an account of his experiences to the Earl of Dartmouth.[1]

On all the houses, window-shutters, and doors in the approach to Birmingham, and on every house there, was written 'Church and King for ever.' I met the crier on horseback . . . distributing his papers to the multitude. Every shop shut. Many of the principal inhabitants fled out of town. The mob were, at the time I was in Birmingham, assaulting Mr. William Russell's house at Moseley Wake Green. Captain Keir at the great house, Hill Top, was chair-man at the meeting of the Revolutionists. He expects the mob, has provided arms &c. and means to stand on his defence.

This proclamation and subsequent ones had been issued with Aylesford's authority and addressed the rioters as 'fellow churchmen'. There is no doubt where Jesse's sympathies lay, for his regret at these events had nothing to do with justice or charity.

Though I smiled and was much pleased to read the old toast 'Church and King' on every house, I am very sorry for the occasion. I fear this opposition will give strength to the opposed.

[1] Hist. MSS. Comm., Rep. 15, App. I, vol. iii, 272 f.

He went on to say that Lord Aylesford had been very active from the beginning of the confusion 'and offered his person to be exposed to the greatest danger'. But if, as the Dissenters found reason to believe, the outrage had been planned but had gone further than intended, then Aylesford, who was a most zealous church-and-king man and lord lieutenant of the county, would not seem to have been in much personal danger. This appears to be confirmed in the following account by Jesse himself. On the Friday, before very many of the mob had left Fair Hill, Aylesford had gone out to them there; he called to the ringleaders, who came round him, and they all shouted 'Aylesford for ever.' He then marched them off to Birmingham, but when they arrived no one knew what to do with them; no arrests were made, and they were left to carry on as they wished. Several of Priestley's and (later) Russell's papers were believed by the mob to be in Aylesford's hands, and of such a serious nature as to be forwarded to London.

But not all those in high circles approved Aylesford's action in acknowledging the rabble as fellow churchmen. The Earl of Claremont, writing to a friend in Belfast, said: [1]

The Birmingham brutes, as you justly call them, are a disgrace to humanity, and the letter of the gentlemen is, if possible, worse than the outrages of the rabble.

There is some reason to believe that nothing more was intended at first than a demonstration against the Old and New Meetings. The New Meeting was not registered, and so had no legal right to exist as a religious building for the holding of services. No charge, indeed, was preferred against any of the rioters for attacking it. One rioter was accused of demolishing the Old Meeting, but the charge was dismissed when the record of registration, dated 1689, was produced, and it was found to refer to an earlier building in a nearby street.

What happened afterwards was considered to have been unreasonable and excessive, but not all those near the throne were unduly perturbed by it. Thus the Marquis of Buckingham, writing from Stowe to Lord Grenville, told of a later attack

[1] Hist. MSS. Comm., Rep. 13, App. VIII, ii, 141.

against the house of John Taylor.[1] But, he added, 'I may say in confidence to you, that I am not sorry even for this *excess, excessive as it has been.*' Such an admission to one who a few months earlier had been made Secretary of State for foreign affairs, and especially charged with matters relating to France, is particularly revealing. Even the King, when authorizing Dundas, as home secretary, to send troops to Birmingham, felt no compunction in admitting: [2] 'I cannot but feel better pleased that Priestley is the sufferer for the doctrines he and his party have instilled, and that the people see them in their true light.' Pitt did nothing to suggest regret, and Burke, who was at Margate when the news arrived, could scarcely contain his joy.

Priestley's antagonists among the clergy of Birmingham continued their paper war for some time afterwards. The so-called 'ministerial' papers, such as *The Times*, were allowed to repeat what was, in fact, the story told to the mob. *The Times* of 19 July, like the second handbill, by giving an incorrect account of the dinner and the toasts, represented those who had attended as republicans and regicides. 'The King's head on a charger' was attributed to Priestley, who was not even present. Grenville's information from Buckingham, also dated 19 July, said that the treasonable toast was everywhere credited in Birmingham.

Whatever interpretation is given to these events, it still remains true that the mob's actions on the first three days appeared to follow a definite plan. Withering, almost the last to be visited, was quite convinced that there was a list of objectives, and that during the riots the list was altered. Hutton, who suffered, not as a Dissenter, but as a particularly active Commissioner of the Court of Requests, said that every mob had its owner, and this one was owned by some of the principal inhabitants. 'There is too much reason to believe the superiors wished to raise the mob, and fatally succeeded, and I believe they afterwards wished to lay it but could not.' Still there would have been no riots had not suitable instruments been found—'a hungry Attorney, and a leading Justice', who,

---

[1] Hist. MSS. Comm., Rep. 14, App. V, vol. ii, 133.
[2] B. Dobrée (Ed.), *The Letters of King George III*, London, 1935, 212.

Hutton thought, expected to receive some reward for their efforts. Certainly there was method in the riots.[1]

First, as Buckingham said, the false story about the dinner was circulated and generally credited. Secondly, it was also believed that some thousands of leaflets had been found in Priestley's house ready for distribution. The mob was told that John Taylor had paid for the printing of them, and this, more than anything else, had set them off to take revenge on his property. This, too, was reported by Buckingham. Thirdly, while Russell's house was in flames, two men arrived on horseback and read out forged letters claimed to have been found among Priestley's and Russell's papers. These, among other things, said that the Dissenters as a body had decided to assemble on 16 August 'to burn the churches, blow up the parliament, cut off the head of the king, and abolish all taxes'. This introduced the final stage of assault on the property of Dissenters at large. The Committee of Dissenters subsequently offered a reward of one hundred pounds for the discovery of the writer of these letters.

Being inflamed by such false information, the mob, after demolishing the homes of Priestley and Russell, had gone on to destroy, burn, or plunder the home of John Ryland (formerly the house of John Baskerville at Easy Hill); Bordesley Hall and several houses belonging to John Taylor; Hutton's town and country houses; the mansion of George Humphrys, near Priestley's house at Sparkbrook; Moseley Hall and other property in the vicinity; a meeting-house and minister's house at Kingswood; a farm at Worstock, and another at Solihull; estates at Ladywood and Five Ways; and Withering's mansion, Edgbaston Hall.

Orders from Dundas reached Nottingham early on the Sunday morning, and three troops of the 15th Regiment of dragoons left at 10.30 a.m. on horseback, reaching Erdington, four miles outside Birmingham, soon after 7 p.m. They entered the town at about 10 p.m., thousands having gone out to meet them. There was great acclamation, and the streets were illuminated. The town was immediately restored almost to

---

[1] For more details see R. B. Rose, 'The Priestley Riots of 1791', *Past and Present*, November 1960, No. 18, 68–88.

normal, although on the Monday groups of rioters went off towards King's Norton, Bromsgrove, and Halesowen, making demands on the country people as they went. On Tuesday night a house was attacked, but Aylesford left immediately to investigate and found, on arrival, that the rioters had been overpowered by the local residents. Altogether 4,000 troops had received orders to march. Three troops of light dragoons arrived on the Wednesday, and three troops of dragoon guards on the Friday. Some time after, 500 men of the 31st Regiment of foot and three troops of the Oxford Blues were sent to remain as long as necessary to secure the safety of the citizens and the normal continuance of the great trade of the town.

Chapter 14

Rough Justice

The Times, whose first report of the Revolution Dinner was grossly inaccurate, proved in the main to have been well informed. Priestley had been traced to the house of a relative in the country, and subsequently to Kidderminster, and the mob intended to follow him there. Certain papers found at Priestley's house had come into the hands of 'Mr Parker, a very eminent attorney' and had been transmitted to the Secretary of State. Ryland's house had been marked for destruction because his son had helped Priestley to escape. All this, it later appeared, was true. And so, probably, was the widely believed story that the rioters had intended to take Priestley's life. 'The insurgents of Birmingham had made a gridiron of immense size, which they brought to Doctor Priestley's house, where they said they meant to broil an anti-constitutional philosopher, by the blaze of his own writings, and light the fire with the *Rights of Man*.'

When *The Times* received a complaint from Priestley himself, the editor admitted that he had been imposed upon, and retracted his first story. The report of the treasonable toast and the rumour that incendiary papers had been found at Fair Hill were both without foundation. The editorial articles also made some astute comments on the nature of the riots. The mob was very numerous, but the number of those who took an active part was small, and they appeared to be skilled in the work of demolition. There were other disquieting features. The normal fury and confusion, without discrimination of persons, were lacking. A particular group of men were singled out as objects of popular vengeance, and no others suffered. This, the paper thought, was a matter for astonishment.

On 30 July a Royal proclamation called for the rioters to be apprehended and brought to justice, and for some time the events in Birmingham again formed a major topic of national news. On 2 August *The Times* devoted its leading article to the subject, and defended its policy, though declaring its 'utter abhorrence of the mobility taking the executive power into their own hands'.

Notwithstanding the many Letters we have received on the subject of the Birmingham Riots, and the French Revolution, disapproving of what has appeared on those subjects, in this paper, we still remain firmly persuaded that the celebration in England of what happened in France to cause that Revolution, was an unwise, improper, and dangerous measure for any sett of men to adopt.

The paper had already pointed out that Lord Stanhope, and R. B. Sheridan, the playwright and politician, had—at the personal request of the Prince of Wales—declined to attend the Revolution Dinner in London, and it now admitted that Priestley had taken no part in the proceedings at Birmingham.

Under these circumstances, the Doctor, we must acknowledge, has been cruelly treated, and we do most sincerely, with every man who admires Genius, lament the loss of his valuable philosophical apparatus—of his library and his manuscripts. Their destruction is irreparable . . .

Subsequently the paper accurately reported the trials at the Warwick Assizes, and was incensed at the leniency shown by the jury. It realized, however, that this was due largely to the mental confusion of principles that had resulted from the struggle of the different parties in the town. The trials showed men swearing to facts, about which they could not easily be mistaken, in direct contradiction to one another, and provided 'the most shocking proofs of the degree to which men's minds may be perverted by the rancour of party zeal'.

The common citizens, indeed, could scarcely be blamed for thinking that the riots, at least in the early stages, had not caused much offence in high quarters. On the first day of the trials, two of the three prisoners were acquitted. But on the second day, when three men were charged with pulling down Priestley's house, the prosecuting counsel plainly told the jury where its duty lay. It was being said in the streets that the men stood a good chance of acquittal on political grounds. 'Contradict it, Gentlemen, for it is to your disgrace if you do not.'

At this the foreman of the jury interrupted, incidentally showing that he had no liking for the task that had been thrust upon him.

I told your Lordship yesterday that I wished to decline serving at all . . . I feel it, that the learned counsel has insinuated that we have done wrong . . .

The judge, Sir Richard Perryn, thought that counsel's comments were justified. But any friend of Church and King who had lived through the events of the last few months must have been brought up with a shock on hearing the rights of citizens now stated plainly.

Dr Priestley, in his public and private character, is an honour to society, and if he is to have his house pulled down because he holds particular religious doctrines and political opinions, you ought to sell your property in the country, and leave it immediately . . . if I had been at Birmingham, I would have lost my life in the protection of his house, and the more so because he holds opinions different from mine . . . Every man has a right to hold his particular opinion, and if you do not convict you are enemies of your country . . .

Gentlemen . . . Dr. Priestley's house was pulled down because he was a Dissenter; you know very well that is no reason at all; Dr. Priestley's life is irreproachable. I believe he would not have escaped with life if he had stayed half an hour longer . . .

Gentlemen . . . you stand in a very conspicuous situation, there are no twelve men in England upon whom the whole country are looking with so much anxiety and expectation as upon you . . .

Two of the three were found guilty; the third, about whose intentions some doubt existed, was acquitted. After this several other cases were tried, but they were not pressed with the same vigour, and there was only one more conviction. Altogether four men were found guilty; two of them received the King's pardon, and the other two, already confirmed criminals, were executed at Warwick on 8 September.

The noise created by Priestley's enemies and denigrators, though loud and sustained, was not enough to drown the voice of sympathy that made itself heard throughout Europe, and it was this that the Government feared. Lansdowne, Stanhope, Sheridan, and Fox stood by him personally and by the cause he represented. Letters were received, and some of them published in the papers and elsewhere, from various societies in France, especially those of the Friends of the Constitution in Paris, Nantes, Strasbourg, and Rennes, as well as the Academy of Sciences. In August he had a message from the Committee of the Revolution Society in London, and in September an address from the students at Hackney. On 1 September, at the quarterly meeting of dissenting laymen and ministers of the West Riding, held at the Strafford's Arms, Wakefield, those present were stimulated by the recent events to draw up an address to the nation, stating the grounds of their Protestant Dissent and declaring their satisfaction at the revolution in France. At the same time Priestley's successor at Leeds and two other representatives were instructed to prepare a second address, expressing the concern of the meeting for his sufferings.

During the same period, party spirit became more intense. Although Priestley's congregation at Birmingham pressed him to return, it proved impossible for him to do so, and he was also warned not to attempt to visit his friends in Manchester. For such reasons he found it necessary to pass the time with friends at Missenden, and then Hackney and Tottenham. Eventually he decided that it would be safest and best to stay in the neighbourhood of London. When this was known, many people again rallied to his support. John Wilkinson found him a house at Clapton, near Hackney (and close to several of his friends and acquaintances, such as Belsham, William Stone, and others connected with the New College); Wilkinson also gave Priestley £500, and sent £5,000 to Benjamin Vaughan to invest in the French funds on his behalf. Priestley sent the rest of his capital, about £1,500, to John Vaughan to invest in the American funds.[1] He now had a stake in two other countries, so that he could leave at any time if it became too dangerous to remain in England. When making his gifts, Wilkinson gave his opinion that it would be best to emigrate:

[1] Samuel Vaughan, a wealthy West Indian merchant, is said to have made presents to influential people to ensure the favourable reception of his sons. In 1785 he gave Washington an elaborately carved mantelpiece still to be seen in the banquet room at Mount Vernon.

It is pretty evident to me that there are Bigots in this country who think it would be of service to what they call our Holy Religion, to have you destroyed by any means. How far you are out of their reach where you now are, I am not able to determine, but I am of this opinion, that the spirit which at present seems to reign could not affect you as readily in its operations in France as it may in this Country . . .

Priestley's sympathizers in France thought the same. He first received an offer of a completely furnished house near Paris, and this was followed on 4 October 1791 with a flattering address from a society at Toulouse, inviting him to the South of France, where a vacant monastery could be put at his disposal. He had, however, definitely decided to live at Hackney. There Price's former congregation, with some courage, invited him to be their minister. About a quarter of them voted against this, on the grounds that with Priestley and the college in the vicinity there might be further civil disturbances. Somewhat uneasily he remained there for more than two years, preaching, and lecturing on science and history.

Priestley went to his new home in September 1791, and immediately set about reconstructing his library and laboratory. Though he succeeded far beyond what many thought possible, chiefly through the help of Wilkinson, Withering, Wedgwood, and the latter's son, Thomas, he was unable to settle down to productive work. Nevertheless, by the end of the year he was once again installed more or less in the manner to which he had now grown accustomed.

In the meantime, with the help of friends, benefactors, booksellers, and instrument makers, he began to assess the value of the property that had been damaged and destroyed in the riots, a task that was not only painful but unusually difficult, in view of the unique way in which his possessions had been assembled. The estimates were at last completed, and he also wrote an *Appeal* to justify his behaviour and to ask for, or rather insist on, a fair interpretation of the events that had led to the riots. He did his utmost to live quietly and to give no possible cause of offence—and tried to use his influence with the students at the college to make them act cautiously and soberly in all matters connected with politics.

His house was rather larger than he needed, for his family was now dispersing: Joseph at Manchester, Sally at Heath, Harry at Bristol, and William shortly to be sent to France again. He hoped to find William a position through the good offices of Count Français Antoine, now simply M. Français (who had founded a society of Friends of the Constitution at Nantes in 1790 and became President of the National Assembly in June 1792), and the duc de la Rochefoucauld d'Enville, now simply M. Rochefoucauld.

The first few months of Priestley's residence at Clapton were uneventful, though it could scarcely be said that he was welcome there. Shopkeepers, workmen, and servants shunned the Priestleys and their house. It was difficult to find people willing to work for them in any capacity. Though there was no perceptible change in the attitude of his political associates, with whom he occasionally dined, his scientific friends in the Royal Society treated him distantly, perhaps fearing to be associated with him. He particularly regretted that Cavendish avoided him, for they had enjoyed a friendly and useful association for a quarter of a century. But he understood their reaction, as he did that of his friends in Manchester—'thus the chased deer is avoided by all the herd'. As they appeared to wish it, he reluctantly withdrew from them, and longed again for the Lunar Society meetings, to which he continued to be invited, though it proved impossible for him to venture there.

The press, the public prints, and the Anglican pulpits continued their attacks, even when the damage caused by the riots was being assessed in the King's bench, and attempts were made, even at that hour, to destroy any popular sympathy for those Dissenters whose claims were being considered. None of the plaintiffs was allowed anything near the amount of damages asked for. Priestley's personal claim amounted to £4,083 10s 3d.[1] The value of the apparatus and scientific equipment destroyed was estimated at £602 2s by Messrs Nairne & Blunt, mathematical instrument makers of Cornhill, London, books at £432 15s 6d, papers and manuscripts at £420 15s—as compared with £1,307 8s for household goods and furniture, and £1,267 4s

[1] Described by D. McKie, *Notes & Records*, 1956, *12* (1), 129.

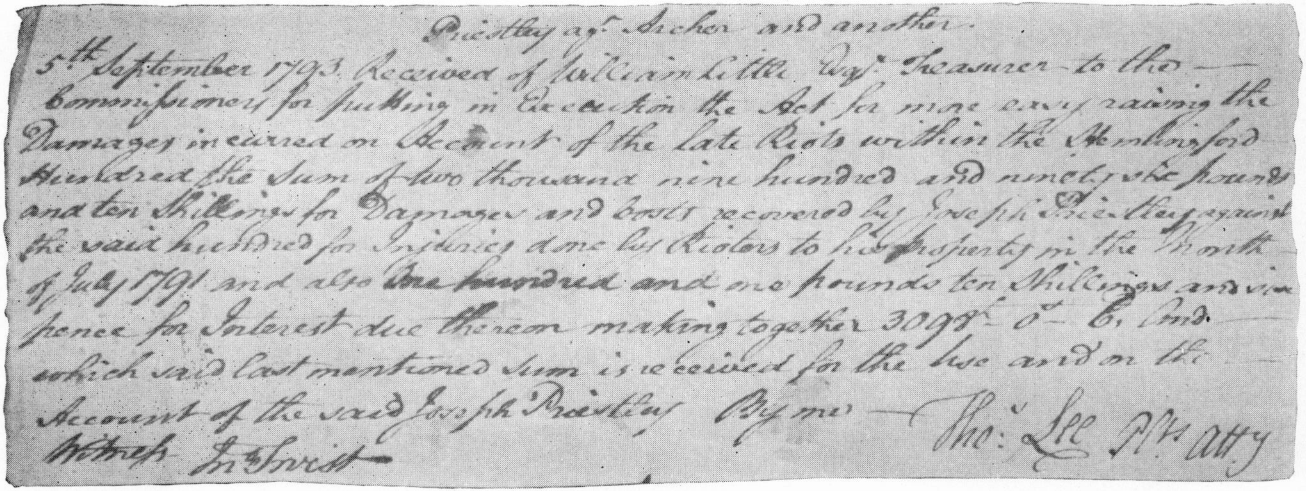

Priestley agt. Archer and another

5th September 1793 Received of William Little Esqr. Treasurer to the Commissioners for putting in Execution the Act for more easy raising the Damages incurred on Account of the late Riots within the Hemlingford Hundred the Sum of two thousand nine hundred and ninety six pounds and ten Shillings for Damages and Costs recovered by Joseph Priestley against the said hundred for Injuries done by Rioters to his property in the Month of July 1791 and also one hundred and one pounds ten Shillings and sixpence for Interest due thereon making together 3098 – 0 – 6. And which said last mentioned Sum is received for the use and on the Account of the said Joseph Priestley By me — Tho: Lee Plts atty

Witness Jno Twist

Plate 17 Receipt signed by Priestley's Attorney or £3,098 0s 6d recovered from the Hemlingford Hundred 'for Injuries done by Rioters to his property'. (*Warwickshire Records Office*)

Plate 18 Priestley's home (large house in left foreground) at Northumberland, Pennsylvania, at the confluence of the western and north-eastern branches of the Susquehanna. Sunbury is shown in the background. From an original sketch by a French visitor, the Count de Maulevrier (M. Colbert). (*Courtesy Johns Hopkins Press, Baltimore*)

for damage to the buildings. Altogether he was allowed damages and costs of £2,996 10s. Part of this represented the expense of preparing the claim, and Priestley doubtless felt the need for ready money. But the months slipped by, and still no action was taken by the authorities to raise the money in order to pay the sums awarded. Eventually Pitt himself felt obliged to make inquiries; it appeared that assistance would be required in order to raise the estimated total of £33,000 which included the legal costs of dealing with the claims.

The Earl of Aylesford, who was called upon to answer Pitt's questions, seems to have foreseen difficulties in raising even this reduced sum through rates on the Hemlingford Hundred, and he was forced to work out a plan whereby this could be done without causing further unrest. At long last, in the early months of 1793, he obtained an Act of parliament 'for the more easy raising Money upon the Hundred of *Hemlingford* . . . than is authorized to be done by the Laws now in being'. By this act, the Justices of the Peace and two knights of the shire were appointed Commissioners and empowered to borrow part of the money by an issue of debentures, time being allowed for their repayment, and the books being open to inspection by any ratepayer. In addition, no proceedings were permitted to be brought by the 'sufferers' in order to recover their money until after 29 September 1793.

The first meeting of the Commissioners was held at the Swan Inn, Coleshill, on 22 June 1793, at which it was recorded that loans of £6,000 each would be forthcoming from the two banking firms of Taylor & Lloyd, and Spooner Attwoods & Aynsworth. On 26 June a treasurer was appointed, and debentures made out in respect of loans now amounting to £16,200. On 1 July the debentures were executed; an assessment was ordered on the Hemlingford Hundred for raising a first instalment of £11,337, and warrants were ordered to be delivered to the petty constables throughout the Hundred to that end.

By 31 August most of the constables had produced the amounts assessed on their districts, but those of Meriden and Birmingham had failed to do so by the stipulated time. It was decided to take action against them, but the threat appears to

15

have been sufficient. At last, drafts were made out for the payment of all awards to the sufferers, and on 5 September the treasurer was ordered to pay all outstanding claims.

The receipt from Priestley's attorney at Birmingham shows that he received £3,098 0s 6d (Plate 17). The claim had taken almost two years to settle. In January 1794 it was agreed that Aylesford should be paid all his expenses in full, and that the debentures should be paid off during 1794 and 1795. This was effected by raising four separate assessments on the Hundred— in July 1793, April and October 1794, and April 1795. By that time Priestley had left the country.[1]

As feeling in England hardened against the French, so distrust fell more and more on Priestley and those of his friends who had dealings with that country. He first experienced real concern on that score in 1792 when he read in the *Morning Chronicle* that his son William had applied for naturalization and had been introduced to the National Assembly by M. Français de Nantes on 7 June. In this connection Français delivered an encomium of Priestley the father, to show the son's worthiness. Among other things, he said that Priestley was the man who, 'by discovering the different weights of the several kinds of air, had prepared for the imagination of our Country that brilliant invention which has extended the domain of man to another element', that is the conquest of air by balloons. Priestley, he added, had always lived far from intrigue and ambition. The incident was reported on 9 June in the *Moniteur*, from which it had been picked up by the London papers. Lindsey correctly foresaw that it would give a new topic to the cartoonists (Plate 16) and a fresh excuse for abusing the Dissenters. Wilkinson alone seems to have been pleased with the notice that was being taken of the youth. On 25 June 1792 Priestley wrote to his son: [2]

Dear William,
    I hope you will attend to what your mother says in her part of the letter. Remember you are to be a *man of business*, and I hope you will not let the attention that has been paid to you by the National

---

[1] The Warwick Quarter Session Records have also been examined by R. E. W. and F. R. Maddison, *Notes & Records*, 1957, *12*, 98.
[2] P. A. S., in *Notes & Queries*, 1867, *11* (3S), 186.

Assembly hurt your mind, or lead you to expect any particular advantage farther than a good introduction and a good connection.

He then gave his son a business commission, possibly to bring his thoughts back to everyday matters.

Mr. B. Vaughan is not now in England. Perhaps he may find you at Paris. However, I believe he has employed Mr. Peregaux the banker (No. 19, Rue du Sentier), about my money in the Funds, as I had a letter from him about it. You will therefore call on Mr. Peregaux (he is your uncle's banker); and if it be so, show him this letter, to authorize him to pay you the interest as it comes due. If any other form be necessary, it shall be complied with as soon as I know it.

Finally he added some general points, showing his interest in what was taking place in France, and using this as a means of trying to get more letters from the young man, both for himself and for Wilkinson.

I have written to Mr. Français on the subject of your naturalization, and shall be glad to know whether the letter has reached him. I am much interested in what is now passing at Paris, and wish you would write often and fully. I am glad that Mr. Français and Mr. Rochefoucauld think well of your affairs.

The Times referred to the episode on a number of occasions, but by now made no pretence at reporting facts. Already on 14 June it had said:

It is asserted that the reception of the Birmingham hero in the National Assembly, has determined his Reverend Sire to follow him to that land of liberty—and in order to render himself the more acceptable, he has chartered a vessel to be freighted with his own writings, Tom Paine's *Rights of Man*, &c. &c.—which he means to present to that August Body for the purpose of making cartridges for the use of the troops.—This is well considered—as their combustible quality, no doubt, will prove a prodigious saving in the article of gun-powder.

There was to be no respite for Priestley while the revolution became progressively more dismal to English eyes. On 20 June the Paris mob forced its way into the Tuileries and threatened the King, and in July volunteers from all parts of France marched to Paris with petitions calling for his deposition. On

10 August 1792 a more alarming insurrection caused Louis to take refuge in the hall of the Legislative Assembly, and there his suspension was pronounced. As a result the National Convention was called into being, which among other things brought Robespierre to power.

On 26 August a law was enacted by which several foreigners were created French citizens—a doubtful honour at that stage in the country's affairs, as it seemed in London, especially as they singled out men who, 'by their writings, and by their valour, have served the cause of liberty, and prepared the emancipation of nations'. It declared that 'the title of French citizen is conferred on Doctor Joseph Priestley, on Thomas Paine, on Jeremy Bentham; on William Wilberforce . . . George Washington . . .', and others.

Bentham was amused by this wording. In 1796 he wrote to Wilberforce:

Don't let it mortify you too much, but *we three* (two P and a B) were made grandees of the first class,—set down *in petto* for Solons,— fenced off from the *gens en sous ordre* by a semicolon—an *impayable* semicolon! We being thus intrenched and enthroned, after us they let in a parcel of corn-consumers,—the *Wilberforces*, the *Washingtons* . . .

But at the time it was not amusing to be the first named on the list. On 3 September, Lord Grenville received a report from Paris that Paine was there and had been appointed to a post in the government. 'Dr. Priestley is also there, and is consulted on all occasions by the new Ministers.' Others from Manchester, Scotland, and London, including William Stone, were busily engaged in the fabrication of democratic papers, intended to be printed in France and then sent to England and Ireland for distribution. However, there is no reason to believe that Priestley had visited Paris, for no such report reached the papers, and *The Times* of 10 September printed a pretended letter from Paine saying that the sons of freedom were panting for Priestley's arrival there.

On 5 September 1792 Priestley was elected a member of the Convention by the Departments of Orne and Rhône-et-Loire, receiving more than one-half of the possible number of votes. This honour he declined, though he asked permission to make known his views on matters under consideration. This he did through correspondence with his friends, chiefly Vaughan and Stone. He also exhorted the Convention to avoid illegal violence and internal dissension, which dishonoured the cause of liberty.

But such advice went unheeded. On 21 September the Convention pronounced the abolition of the monarchy. Soon afterwards it was decided that the King should be brought to trial, and in December he faced several charges of treason. In January 1793 sentence of death was passed on him, despite the strong objections of some of the new citizens, especially Priestley and Bentham. On 21 January he was guillotined. On 27 February John Adams wrote, in a letter that Priestley passed to Shelburne: 'I think that all the ages and nations of the world never furnished so strong an argument against a pure republic as the French have done.'

During these months the atmosphere in England had been electric. Waves of panic struck the populace, and there were fears of secret plots and conspiracies to overthrow the monarchy and destroy the constitution. Multitudes thronged to the Court to testify their loyalty. As Lindsey said of those days, no obloquy and abuse was thought too gross to be vented against the Dissenters, and against Priestley by name, and this drew from Mrs Barbauld a courageous poem, which was printed in the *Morning Chronicle* on 8 January 1793.

> Stirs not thy spirit, Priestley, as the train
> With low obeisance and with servile phrase,
> File behind file, advance with supple knee,
> And lay their necks beneath the foot of power ?
> Burns not thy cheek indignant, when thy name,
> On which delighted science lov'd to dwell,
> Becomes the bandied theme of hooting crowds?

This was the end of Priestley's work in England. If his struggle for civil and religious liberty was to have any further effect, it would have to come from his writings and from the memories cherished in many minds that from now on could expect to find little freedom for expression. But all this would pass. Another generation would take up the fight, and eventually a free and tolerant England would remember him with gratitude.

. . . Scenes like these hold little space
In his large mind, whose ample stretch of thought
Grasps future periods.—Well can'st thou afford
To give large *credit* for that debt of fame
Thy country owes thee. Calm thou can'st consign it
To the slow payment of that distant day,
If distant, when thy name, to freedom's join'd,
Shall meet the thanks of a regenerate land.

On the death of Louis in January all hope of peace vanished; war was declared in February. A new outburst of fury against those who had sympathized with the revolution, and against the Dissenters, created alarm in several parts of the country, and many who could afford to do so seriously considered emigrating to America. Priestley for the first time felt really unsafe, and his wife, who had remained optimistic until this, now began to be apprehensive. To Wilkinson he wrote: 'I can give you no idea of the rancour that is now more than ever prevalent against me, as it shows itself in hand bills, and every other way calculated to excite mischief.' He was also being attacked by Burke and others in the House of Commons. In March 1793 a new law was introduced to prevent correspondence with France, but just before this William had written to say that he would leave for America as soon as he could. 'No son of mine,' wrote Priestley, 'can ever settle in this country unless things should take a turn that we have no reason to expect.'

Soon the violence of party spirit was such that the family began to plan for emigration. William, it was hoped, had already left France. Joseph had decided to leave Manchester, if possible with Cooper and Thomas Henry junior. Harry, who had been brought from Bristol to study the classics at Hackney under Gilbert Wakefield, found that several of his companions at the New College were planning to occupy land in America, and asked to go as well. Vaughan's sons promised to look after him, and so Priestley had consented. Sally, unfortunately, would be unable to leave Dudley. This, and the fact that his damages had not yet been paid, were the only reasons that made it seem worth staying for a while until his sons had crossed the Atlantic and prepared a new home.

On 4 March, in the House of Commons, Sheridan had found occasion to mention the unjust treatment from which Priestley was still suffering, and particularly the lack of compensation for the loss of his property in Birmingham. He had also been accused of poisoning the New River water supply, and the company had been forced to deny this false report in the newspapers before the public would believe that it was unfounded. Burke continued his abuse, and on 7 March Priestley wrote a letter to *The Times* challenging him to substantiate his remarks. He reminded Burke that he had nothing to do with the Revolution Society's correspondence with France, nor was he a member of any political society whatever. What authority, he asked, could Burke produce for saying that he had been made a citizen of France because of his declared hostility to the constitution of England?

In May he heard much talk of a scheme to establish a liberal college in America; if this came into being he proposed to leave and devote himself to it. Lindsey and he had agreed to give their libraries, and, with Priestley's apparatus, this would give them a good start. The college in Hackney, he thought, was destined to failure, as the funds had been spent improvidently and few people would now be willing to contribute to its support.

In June the outlook was 'peculiarly dark and discouraging'. He could see no consolation anywhere. His wife had been ill, spitting blood; his old gall-stone complaint had returned; and the thought of being separated from all his sons made him melancholy at times. But he still had not received his damages, which he had arranged to transfer to John Vaughan in Philadelphia to invest in the American funds. During the waiting period he tried hard to fight off all depression, and, with his sons, whose passage had been delayed, made a study of *American Geography*, a copy of which had been lent to him by the author, Jedidiah Morse, who was engaged on the far side of the Atlantic in helping emigrants to settle there. His sons took the book with them when they sailed late in August 1793 from Gravesend. The ship, Priestley said, was crowded with passengers, as was every other vessel bound for America. In his letter of thanks for the book Priestley wrote: [1]

Reproduced by M. C. Park (see p. 223).

We had but an imperfect idea of America before, and it has contributed not a little to the spirit of emigration that now prevails in this country. But the chief incentive is the increasing spirit of bigotry encouraged by the court, that makes it very unpleasant and almost unsafe, for the friends of liberty civil or religious to continue here. One of my sons will deliver this, and it is my wish to fetch them all with you, in order to follow them myself some time hence . . . Great numbers would go, if they knew how to get to America, or how to live there when they were there.

Soon harsher measures began to be adopted against those who still spoke out in favour of reforms. Priestley learnt in August that one of his acquaintances in Manchester was being accused of training men to join the French and of using seditious language. More serious still, Thomas Muir, a member of the Faculty of Advocates of Edinburgh who had taken part in promoting a society for obtaining parliamentary reform, was accused of disloyalty and of distributing seditious literature, and harshly sentenced to fourteen years' deportation. In September, Thomas Fysche Palmer, a convert of Priestley and Lindsey who had established a unitarian congregation in Dundee, was sentenced to seven years' deportation for being associated with a publication that called the war-time taxation extravagant, and that demanded universal suffrage and short parliaments.

By this time Priestley had received his compensation money, which he soon disposed of—£900, ordered to be paid over to George Humphrys in Birmingham, and £2,000 to John Vaughan in Philadelphia for settlement on his sons William and Henry. Now the question was no longer whether to emigrate, but only when. He wished first to see two scientific items through the press—*Experiments on the Generation of Air from Water* (1793), addressed to the Lunar Society, and *Heads of Lectures on . . . Experimental Philosophy* (1794), in which he outlined the course he had given at the New College, and gave his parting advice to the students on the best way to conduct themselves in those times of stress and danger.

By the new year he had received favourable news from Joseph in America, but from Europe came nothing but gloomy reports. From Stone he learnt that the French intended to invade England, and it seemed possible that an attempt might be made at any time. He badly wanted to apply to the National Convention about the payment of interest on his investments there, but was warned that it would not be safe to do so while he remained in England. It had been hinted to him by another friend that a letter was on its way to him from New York, with an invitation to take charge of a department in the College there; he hoped this would prove true, as it would make his departure easier and 'more reputable'.

In February 1794, with all his friends urging him to leave as soon as he could—lest he should share the fate of Muir, Palmer, and several others who were shortly to be sent to Botany Bay— he booked passages for himself and his wife, together with a servant-girl and a boy, in an American vessel due to sail at about the end of March. He began to pack his apparatus, and issued an advertisement to the effect that the lease on the house and the furniture would be sold by auction. He then packed his books. Before leaving, he hoped to conclude a final series of discourses on scriptural revelation, which he was simultaneously seeing through the press, but apart from this little remained to be done.

As the day of departure approached, their spirits rose, and Mary Priestley especially looked forward excitedly to the voyage. To avoid any misunderstanding at that hour, Priestley made it perfectly clear on several occasions that he was going to America, and that he was leaving of his own choice. He told the American ambassador, so that he could pass the information to Paris, in order to safeguard his property there. To ensure that the government should be aware of his plans, he wrote to Eden, now Lord Auckland, to obtain a 'protection' for his party in case the vessel should be captured on the high seas. This letter, dated from Clapton on 25 March 1794, has been preserved; it effectively answers the stories circulated by William Cobbett and others which made it appear that Priestley had left England furtively and secretly in order to avoid government action against him.

Having occasion to apply to some person near the seat of power, I have no hesitation from our former acquaintance, and my real esteem for your Lordship, to have recourse to you.

Being about to leave this country, I am desirous of doing it with as much security as I can; and as the ship in which I go is an American (the Sansom, Capt Smith for New York) liable to capture by the Algerenes, I am desirous of getting a protection from this government. A young man who lately went to Philadelphia told me that he had procured one, promising to return it unopened if it should not be wanted, and I am ready to promise the same . . .

The request was immediately granted. Priestley also announced that his farewell sermon would be preached at the Gravel Pit Meeting, Hackney, on 30 March, and in *The Times* on 31 March there appeared a short notice referring to it, and mentioning that he was departing shortly for America.

During the next few days many friends came to pay them a last visit, though they were not without hopes of returning again in more settled times. Among those who were with the Priestleys to the last were the Lindseys, Susan Wedgwood, William Wilkinson, Finch, and Sally.

The *Sansom*, after some delay, sailed on 8 April. Can we hope to read Priestley's thoughts as he looked for the last time upon his native land? To a man of his simple faith, simple words were adequate to all occasions.

I do not pretend to leave this country, where I have lived so long, and so happily, without regret; but I consider it as necessary, and I hope the same good providence that has attended me hitherto will attend me still.

Did he for one moment doubt the worthwhileness of his life's struggles, or harbour bitter thoughts against the England that now wished to be rid of him? Not at all.

When the time for reflection shall come, my countrymen, I am confident, will do me justice.

Chapter 15

In Search of Peace

HENRY WANSEY, a sheep-farmer and clothier from Wiltshire, sailed for the United States of North America in March 1794 to obtain first-hand information of the kind that emigrants would need to know. On arrival at New York he stayed at Mrs Loring's boarding-house near the Battery. Here, from a large dining-room with ample windows, vessels could be seen sailing out of the harbour on the one side and turning up the Hudson on the other. It was a favourite vantage point for those meeting relatives and friends from Europe, and it was here that he found the younger Thomas Henry from Manchester, and Joseph Priestley junior who was awaiting the coming of his parents.

Joseph junior had arrived in the country in October 1793, and at first thought of entering the cotton industry, of which he had gained some knowledge during his work at Manchester. He had inspected a few factories within fifteen miles of New York, but concluded that they would have little scope until the American market expanded through a great increase in the number of settlers. He thereupon considered the possibilities of a land settlement for English immigrants, and he, Thomas Cooper, and Henry formed a company with John Vaughan and others for this purpose.[1] They travelled extensively in the eastern states, and finally decided that a large tract of land lying between the two main branches of the Susquehanna River and near the Loyalsock Creek, offered the greatest promise. It was agreed that the small town of Northumberland, situated in

[1] For details of land transactions, see M. C. Park, *Proc. Delaware Co. Inst. Sci.*, 1947, *11* (1), 1–60 (obtainable from National Lending Library, Boston Spa, Yorks.). Much general information has been collected by Caroline Robbins in 'Honest Heretic: Joseph Priestley in America', *Proc. Amer. Phil. Soc.*, 1962, *106*, 60.

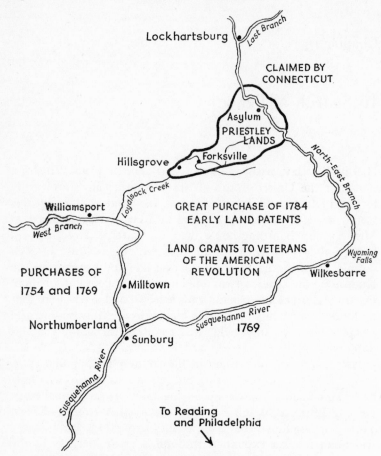

Fig. 12 Part of Pennsylvania, showing the area of the proposed
settlement. (After M.C. Park, *Proc. Delaware Co. Inst. Sci.*, 1947)

the fork of the Susquehanna, would make a suitable head-
quarters for the scheme.

Others were exploring the Loyalsock and the lands of the
Susquehanna's western branch. Thus Woolstoncraft came down
the Loyalsock by canoe at ten miles an hour and was impressed
by the rich bottom lands he saw. He told them that Dr Benjamin
Rush had given him the choice of several four-hundred-acre lots
at five shillings an acre, with six months to pay.

It was on such terms as these that the company proposed to

operate, settlers being able to purchase the land by instalments. An outline of the scheme was sent to Priestley at Hackney, where it reached him in January 1794. When he embarked, he was not without hope that a nucleus of men with similar background and ideals would make the settlement into a kind of outpost of England where the friends of liberty might end their days in peace. In May the younger Joseph was sending copies of the land proposals to friends in England for passing on to anyone likely to be interested. They were acquiring 300,000 acres of land at a dollar an acre, and the capital of the company would consist in 100 shares of 3,000 dollars each. A further 20,000 dollars were to be raised for town improvements, houses for mechanics and tradesmen, and other amenities.

At this time, Wansey, Priestley, and Henry in New York were occupying themselves in making short excursions and social visits. On Sunday, 1 June, they went to service at the new Presbyterian Meeting, where they met the first indication that all might not be easy going when Priestley senior arrived. After the sermon, the congregation was invited to celebrate the Lord's supper, but the minister, with his palm outraised towards Governor Clinton's pew, where Priestley junior and his young wife were sitting, said: 'No, none of those who deny the divinity of our Saviour.' After service they learnt that the *Sansom* had arrived at Sandy Hook, and was waiting for a pilot.

The voyage had taken eight weeks, the ship having been delayed by contrary winds, and for the first five weeks Priestley, and especially his wife, had been sick. On reaching the coast of America they ran into thick fog and rain, and it was not until the evening of Wednesday, 4 June, that the ship entered harbour. Joseph junior took out a boat to meet them, and brought them in as privately as possible to the Battery. His wife took charge of them on landing, and they went immediately to Mrs Loring's. This was soon known throughout New York.

On the following morning they received visits from Governor Clinton, Bishop Prevoost, and Osgood, the former British envoy. Then followed the heads of the College and most of the principal merchants. After this, deputations from the town's corporate body and a number of societies waited on him. As Wansey said, no man in any public capacity could have been received with more respect. Addresses from the various societies, with Priestley's replies, were printed in the newspapers locally, and then circulated throughout the country, and later reprinted in England. In these first public statements since his arrival, Priestley was careful not to include anything of a political flavour.

One other small but significant matter did not pass unnoticed. That year Trinity Sunday fell on 15 June, and certain preachers in New York chose to take advantage of the occasion to show their opposition to Priestley's religious views. They appeared to fear his influence, and had prepared themselves in advance.

After a few days, Joseph junior returned to the settlement, and William took his place. On 18 June they set off for Philadelphia. Though he had been grateful for the warmth of his reception, Priestley had hoped to enter the country quietly, and he was glad to move on. But at Philadelphia he was again 'received with the most flattering attention by all persons of note'. He was pressed to stay there, but found that the cost of living was too great for him. Wansey, who went on to Boston, took with him a letter from Priestley to his former acquaintance, John Adams, now Vice-President. Adams said he would be glad to see him there, and thought Boston might suit him better than any other large American town.

Though it was hot in Philadelphia, and the town at that time lacked certain amenities, such as open spaces and pleasant walks, and was liable to epidemics of yellow fever, it nevertheless held some attractions for him; it was the centre of finance and commerce, of the sciences and the arts. Here also was the American Philosophical Society, of which John Vaughan had become treasurer in 1791, having previously served as secretary, and of which Priestley had been a member since 1785. Before he left the town for Northumberland, it was understood that he was to be offered the Presidency of a new college to be set up in North Carolina, but he let it be known that he had made up his mind to accept no public appointment whatever.

The earlier pattern of his life began to assert itself, and he was soon thinking of living independently at Northumberland and making annual visits to Philadelphia. Yet how different everything proved to be. Though he had been able to dine one day in Birmingham and in London the next, his new journey took five days and was an exhausting experience. In England, correspondence with friends had played a most important part in his life; here it took up to four months to receive a reply from Europe. At first he felt cut off, as good as lost. He missed those on whom he had depended for his physical comfort as well as intellectual stimulation; he was forced for a time into idleness through the absence of a library and laboratory; he was faced with the need to begin life again—in his sixty-second year.

For a long period he had been allowing £15 a year each to his widowed sister Martha and his brother Joshua, and they were soon in his thoughts again on arrival at Northumberland. At the end of July he wrote to Martha, who was living near Leeds. He told her of the voyage, the fortnight in New York, the three weeks in Philadelphia, and the journey to their present home, where they were 'almost out of the world'.

The town is beautifully situated, between two branches of the Susquehannah, each as large as the Thames at London, bounded by rocks and hanging woods . . . The situation is very healthy, and the climate seemingly as good as any in America. We came here to be near to a large settlement that my sons and friends think of making about 50 miles farther up in the country, whither I propose to remove when it is sufficiently advanced for the purpose . . .

The climate and manner of living is so different here from what it is in England, that persons advanced in life cannot expect to be reconciled to it. I feel the difference very sensibly, tho it consists chiefly in little things, and the price of living in the principal towns, being higher than in London, will effectually discourage all emigrations, except of such as are willing to *labour*, the price of this being fully in proportion to every thing else, which is not the case in England. This makes it very difficult to get good servants, and the greater part are Blacks, some free, and some slaves, for servitude is not abolished in all the states . . . certainly I should, on many accounts, have preferred to live in England.

Mary Priestley, whom he now wished to indulge as much as he could, was 'happy and thankful to meet with so sweet a situation and so peaceful a retreat'. In August she wrote to William Vaughan that 'Dr Priestley also likes it and of his own choice intends to settle here which is more than I hoped for at the time we came up'. Soon there would be a proper road and a stage coach to Philadelphia. She did not want to go any further than this—'we are not at a time of life to keep rambling about . . .'. The country around them had been occupied largely by Americans, Irish, Germans, and Scots, and they were all friendly.

People were coming to the house all the time to view and purchase land, but by the end of October it was found that many of the plots of land were not worth buying. Priestley thought that they had been deceived by the proprietors; the land scheme, he said, was all finished, and he had advised his son Joseph to get a farm and forget all about partnerships. In November, however, things looked less depressing. 'Some purchases in the area will answer very well and several settlers are already on the lands.' He had definitely made up his mind to stay at Northumberland, and part of his library and apparatus had been sent up; the rest would arrive shortly. As there were no suitable permanent houses to be bought, he decided to build one for himself (Plate 18).

Had he not so decided, his life in America might have been very different, for on 11 November 1794 the trustees of the University of Pennsylvania unanimously elected him to the chair of chemistry in place of John Carson, who had died.[1] Priestley considered the idea for a time, and thought of employing Thomas Henry junior as his assistant, for he had already helped his father in this way at the Manchester College of Arts and Sciences, where courses on chemistry were first given in 1783. Eventually, however, he declined, but the vacancy was left open until July 1795, when James Woodhouse was appointed. It was thought in the family that he made this decision chiefly for his wife's sake, but another reason emerges from his correspondence.

Northumberland was developing fast, and if more English families settled in the country beyond, there would be a demand for the type of education provided by the academies in England, and it was this kind of work that Priestley wanted more than

[1] See J. S. Hepburn, 'The Pennsylvania Associations of Joseph Priestley', *J. Franklin Inst.*, 1947, *244*, 68.

Plate 19 John Adams, second President of the U.S.A., whom Priestley first met in 1786 on a tour of the London booksellers. By Asher B. Durand, after the original portrait by Gilbert Stuart. (*Courtesy New York Historical Society*)

Plate 20 Thomas Jefferson, third President of the U.S.A.—a strong admirer of Priestley's scientific, educational, and religious writings. Portrait by Gilbert Stuart. (*Courtesy Bowdoin College Museum of Art, Brunswick, Maine*)

any other. He had already set his heart on the founding of such a college, and had discussed the matter with Vaughan and Rush in Philadelphia. Both had given him warm support, and, indeed, there were many who were anxious that his experience as a teacher should be put to good use in a country where such men were scarce. Benjamin Rush, a member of Congress, a professor in the medical college, and one of the principals of the land company, was probably the most influential of Priestley's friends in the area. Many of the chief landowners agreed to contribute both money and land.

Priestley drew up a proposed curriculum and rules for the management of the college. It was understood that he would give courses of lectures gratis, as he had done at Hackney. He could no longer expect to do any considerable new work in either science or philosophy, and so he would allow the use of his library and apparatus until funds were adequate to supply the college with facilities of its own.

In October that year he wrote to Withering in Birmingham about the Northumberland project, and added that he had been appointed Principal of the college. Building was to begin in the spring of 1796, but funds were small, and progress would be slow. Many of the students would become farmers, and so he badly needed a tutor for natural history and botany. He himself would teach all the other subjects for the time being. 'When our common hall is erected, I shall also make use of it as a chapel, for such is the bigotry of the people in this part of the country, that tho' in every other respect my reception has been very flattering, their pulpits are all shut to me.'

The thought of useful work ahead enabled Priestley once more to get down to writing and experimental work, and by the summer of 1795 he was happily busy again. But he was not free from family troubles. His wife had suffered two further alarming attacks of her old illness, with blood-spitting, and on each successive occasion her recovery was slower and more difficult. In the summer of 1794, his youngest son, Harry, who had been educated as a scholar, but had now turned farmer and was living in an isolated situation in a one-room log house of his own construction, had been struck down by fever, and had since recovered from a second attack. He was now building a two-roomed stone house, for which he even had to make the lime and the kiln. William, who had spent a year with a farmer near Boston, had now returned and was working a part of Harry's land.

Before the end of 1795, Harry was ill a third time, and, to the great distress of his parents, he died on 11 December. By that time, William had married the daughter of a local farmer, and they continued to work the land. As Priestley said to Wilkinson, 'the life they lead, quite solitary in the woods, is such as you cannot easily form an idea of'. In the meantime, Mary Priestley had been confined to her bed, or at least to her room, for about three months. It seemed that she would never be strong again, but the thought of preparing a new home had kept her going, with the help of her son Joseph's wife, Elizabeth Ryland, whom he had married in England.

By February 1796, Mary had recovered sufficiently for Priestley to undertake a visit to Philadelphia for a few months with the express purpose of trying to set up a Unitarian congregation there. He went as the guest of William Russell and his family, and Elizabeth, as an old friend of the Russells, accompanied him. The Russells had taken a year to reach America. Sailing from Falmouth in August 1794, their ship had been overhauled by a French frigate, and they found themselves prisoners until 23 December on a French man-of-war in Brest harbour. They were released to spend the winter in Paris, and eventually reached New York in August 1795.

With Vaughan's help, Priestley was enabled to deliver a series of lectures on religious topics, the first being given on 14 February 1796, at the Universalist chapel on Lombard Street. His friends at Philadelphia must have worked hard in preparation for his visit, for there was a 'numerous, respectable, and very attentive' audience, including many members of Congress and John Adams, who called the discourses learned, ingenious, and useful. But, as Priestley had to admit afterwards, many of them had come merely out of curiosity, and because a series of lectures by a notable Englishman was something new for the town. The more conservative Federalists, and Adams himself, soon ceased to attend, fearing to be regarded as heretics. Though Adams cooled towards him, looking to a future election, George Washington showed himself friendly, inviting Priestley to take tea with him. Washington was not unfamiliar with Priestley's theological writings, and they enjoyed some hours of conversation.

As a sequel to this visit, the first permanently established Unitarian congregation in the New World was organized on 12 June. On 21 August they met in a room made available by the University at Fourth and Arch Streets, constituting themselves as 'The Society of Unitarian Christians of Philadelphia'. They were a small group of British merchants, recent immigrants who, until Priestley's arrival, had been 'wandering sheep without fold or shepherd'. But though Priestley was anxious to see a group formed under his encouragement, he felt unable to become their minister, having already declined the chair of chemistry at the University. They therefore thought of asking the Rev. Harry Toulmin (son of Priestley's friend Joshua Toulmin) who was settled at Lexington in Kentucky. Priestley also wanted him as tutor for the Northumberland Academy, but these plans did not materialize. Only the shell of a building for the Academy was erected during Priestley's lifetime, and for several years the Unitarian Society at Philadelphia contented itself with choosing its own lay readers.

On his return to Northumberland, Priestley found his wife in a low state of health. In July he confided to Wilkinson: 'I dread her illness, and she is so feeble at best.' On 17 September 1796 she died. Of this event Priestley wrote to Wilkinson on 19 September in words that suggest that it was a blow from which he could never recover.

The death of Harry affected her much, and it has hardly ever been out of my mind, tho it is near 9 months since he died; but this is a much heavier stroke. It has been a happy union to me for more than thirty years, in which I have had no care about anything in the world, so that, without any anxiety I have been able to give all my time to my own pursuits. I always said I was only a lodger in her house. She had taken much pleasure in planning our new house, and now that it is advancing apace, and promises to be every thing that she wished it to be, she goes to occupy another. I shall however finish the house, as it is fitted for my use as well as that of a family, and Joseph will live with me in it, for I am not able to manage a house for myself.

Mary Priestley had received every possible attention during her last illness from the wives of Joseph and William.

Priestley realized that his achievements had owed a great deal to his wife's able and conscientious support throughout an unusual career that had known many vicissitudes of fortune.

For contriving and executing any work usually done by women, and some kinds that are often done by men, I hardly think she ever had a superior; and I am sure nothing could exceed her in generosity and disinterestedness. No person ever less attended to any species of self-indulgence, or was more occupied about the wants of others ... There never could be a better mother, and I will add sister too . . .

The death of his wife and of Harry had led to a rearrangement of the family resources. Priestley himself was still relying on the support of Wilkinson and his friends to complete his house, the cost of which would now be double the original estimate, and to continue his literary and scientific work. But only two religious friends—a member of the Rayner family and the Duke of Grafton—were contributing regular sums, and these amounted to no more than £90 a year.

Wilkinson had invested a total of £10,000 in the French funds for Priestley's benefit, and as it was not yet yielding interest, he was allowing him to draw £200 a year. However, John and William Wilkinson had been involved in disputes which had resulted in a suit at law. This, to the surprise of many, led to a large award to William, at a time when John was no longer a man of apparently unlimited means. It seems that he had given instructions for all debts to be called in, for early in November Priestley was brought starkly face to face with the reality of his situation as never before. He was presented with an account which showed that he was indebted to Wilkinson to the extent of $56,219, plus £200 which he had recently drawn. This filled him with great distress, for it was absolutely impossible to begin to meet such a demand. He assured Wilkinson that if he had done wrong in continuing to live on his generosity, it was from a misunderstanding of his intention, not from presumption.

In a state of anxiety he waited nearly three months to hear again from Wilkinson; fortunately his reply greatly eased Priestley's mind. Writing on 25 January 1797 he told Wilkinson that he would never be able to recover from the loss of his wife. 'I feel quite unhinged, and incapable of the exertion I used to make. Having always been very domestic, reading and writing with my wife sitting near me, and often reading to her, I miss her everywhere.' His chief hope was that peace would come, and he could pay Wilkinson one last visit before he died.

At this time he was again in Philadelphia, having come primarily to deliver a second set of religious discourses. But the novelty of his preaching had gone, and they were not well attended. Adams came only once.

At that time, too, he learnt that his son-in-law Finch had failed in business, and consequently he became deeply concerned for Sally. He toyed with the idea of going to France in a last desperate attempt to retrieve the £10,000 Wilkinson had deposited there, and which now seemed the key to the solution of the family's difficulties. Only in this way, he thought, could he help Sally and begin repayments to Wilkinson. His son Joseph dissuaded him, but nevertheless the hint somehow reached France, and the rumour was spread that Priestley would soon be on his way there. In view of the political situation this was a cause of much concern to his friends.

In March 1797 John Adams took office as President, and Priestley, as a supposed friend of France, soon became the object of abuse by the press as much as he had been in England. He had gone so far as to discuss the possibility of a journey to France with the French minister and other French people in Philadelphia. But after this he had returned to Northumberland and stayed there quietly, though in a disturbed state of mind. He had come to regard Philadelphia as a disagreeable place, and to some extent he was right, for in the autumns of 1797, 1798, and 1799 outbreaks of yellow fever were so severe that the life of the town was seriously interrupted. In particular, the Unitarian Society cancelled its meetings from August to November in those years, and lost several of its members. Plans had been made to remove Congress to Washington.

Though Priestley had made no comment on American affairs, the press had been somewhat antagonistic since his arrival. The most damaging attack occurred in a pamphlet written by William Cobbett under the pen-name Peter Porcupine.

Appearing first in Philadelphia in the summer of 1794, it went through several editions, and was reprinted in London. Cobbett also kept up a steady stream of abuse in his paper, *Porcupine's Gazette*, until 1799, when he was forced to leave the country after Rush had been awarded $5,000 damages in a successful libel suit.

In these publications Priestley was represented as the enemy of religion, law, and order in any country he lived in. He hoped to bring about a revolution in England on the French lines, Cobbett said, and to this end found it convenient to be at the head of a religious sect. His so-called sermons at Birmingham had been inflammatory discourses, in which he openly attacked the English constitution. Here it was, Cobbett claimed, that the Doctor beat his drum ecclesiastic, to raise recruits in the cause of rebellion. The press soon swarmed with publications giving voice to his principles, he said. The revolutionists began to form societies all over the country, and lines of communication were established like those of the Jacobin clubs in France. Priestley, according to Cobbett, eventually fled from England secretly to avoid action by the government, after he had been amply compensated for the damage sustained in the riots.

Cobbett also reviled Franklin and Price, the late friends of Priestley. But perhaps his most violent outbursts were directed at Talleyrand, the notorious former Bishop of Autun, who had left France for England at the time of the September massacres, and had then left for America after the passing of Pitt's aliens bill. In London, Talleyrand had made the acquaintance of Shelburne (now the Marquis of Lansdowne), Sheridan, Fox, and Benjamin Vaughan—the circle in which Priestley had moved—and had departed in March 1794 with a letter of introduction to John Vaughan. Like the Priestleys, Talleyrand also bought and sold land, and was one of the few at that period who made a considerable profit. He spent most of his time in Philadelphia, and it was there that Priestley renewed his acquaintance with him, and obtained a promise of help when conditions made it possible for Talleyrand to return to France. This occurred in 1797, when he was appointed minister for foreign affairs in succession to Charles Delacroix. The last thing Talleyrand said to him, Priestley wrote, was that 'he depended on seeing me in France'.

By this time Priestley junior, whose group eventually had an interest in some 700,000 acres of land, had dissolved his partnerships and concentrated on his two farms and other projects, which included the setting up of a brewery at Northumberland and, later, a nursery for English garden plants and fruit trees. Cooper was temporarily out of employment and was living with Priestley senior. In August 1797, Cooper thought of applying for an official post as 'agent for American claims', and Priestley thereupon decided to use any influence he might still have with Adams to secure this appointment for his friend. He wrote to Adams on 12 August, but received no reply, and the application was unsuccessful. For a time Cooper undertook the editorship of the *Sunbury and Northumberland Gazette*.

Some of the measures that Adams adopted seemed undemocratic to many people, especially the supporters of Thomas Jefferson, and in February 1798 Priestley broke his silence on political matters. He contributed an anonymous article in two parts to the *Aurora*, the pro-Jefferson newspaper in Philadelphia. He deplored the fact that the Americans had allowed themselves to become heated and divided among themselves over events in Europe with which they had little concern. He thought it wrong that they should contemplate spending large sums on the provision of armed forces and armed vessels, and in maintaining newly established embassies in remote countries with which America had few dealings, particularly when the country was crying out for the means to develop its industries and to provide public amenities, especially to improve internal communications and to obtain books and scientific equipment, 'of which all the universities and colleges of this country are most disgracefully destitute'.

The country was so divided, he said, that if the government came out strongly in favour either of France or of Great Britain it was not impossible that civil war might follow. This article, though couched in very general terms, amounted to a criticism of the 'folly' of Adams's administration.

Not long after this, Cobbett had another opportunity to smear Priestley's name when a package marked 'Dr. Priestley, in America' was found on board a neutral Danish vessel that had been intercepted by the British early in 1798. This package, which contained letters from John Hurford Stone to Priestley and Benjamin Vaughan, had been forwarded from Paris by a route that was thought to be safe, and the lack of a proper address shows that Stone was now out of touch with his former acquaintances. But Stone had mentioned that preparations were well advanced for an invasion of England. At the same time, in his letter to Vaughan, he had admitted that the French were short of some supplies, particularly alkalis, and thus, presumably, short of gunpowder, too. By asking Vaughan's help in sending a consignment of pearl ash or potash to France, Stone made it appear that they were all greater friends to France than to Great Britain.

Another paragraph could not have failed to cause trouble if it became known.

Whether we shall continue or increase our hostilities towards the United States, is as yet uncertain; all depends on the great operation directing against England . . . John Adams's speech on the opening of congress caused a few smiles; the more so, as it was understood to be a speech full of thunder and menace against France. Nothing is wanting but the interposition of some upright and patriotic citizen, to settle the misunderstanding; but I fear it will not be done in John Adams's time.

The letters having been intercepted, it was a foregone conclusion that they would be published and shown in the worst possible light. They quickly went through several editions on both sides of the Atlantic. The first London edition took the opportunity of warning Priestley's younger admirers of the errors of their ways, by printing on the title-page an extract from Coleridge's 'Religious Musings' of 1794. In this poem, after referring to Milton, Newton, and David Hartley, he alluded to Priestley's voluntary exile: [1]

> Lo! Priestley there, Patriot, and Saint, and Sage!
> Him, full of years, from his lov'd native land,
> Statesmen blood-stain'd, and Priests idolatrous,

---

[1] The original had additional lines after the first, showing that Coleridge had never met Priestley:

> 'Whom that my fleshly eye hath never seen,
> A childish pang of impotent regret
> Hath thrill'd my heart.'

With dark lies maddening the blind multitude,
Drove with vain hate. Calm, pitying, he retired,
And mused expectant on these promised years.

The publication of Stone's letters brought about a general
alarm, which reached Coleridge in April 1798 in his retreat at
Nether Stowey, and was the cause of his poem 'Fears in
Solitude'. It hurt him to think that he was regarded as an enemy
of his country.

. . . Such have I been deemed—
But, O dear Britain! O my Mother Isle!
Needs must thou prove a name most dear and holy
To me, a son, a brother, and a friend,
A husband, and a father! who revere
All bonds of natural love, and find them all
Within the limits of thy rocky shores.

William Hazlitt, who had attended some of Priestley's lectures
at the New College, Hackney, was with Coleridge at the time.
Coleridge, indeed, was still hoping to emigrate and settle near
Priestley in Pennsylvania.

In Philadelphia, Porcupine took up the hue and cry in his
Gazette, reproducing Stone's letters and making full use of the
'explanatory' notes in the pamphlet, in which the names of
Priestley and Talleyrand were linked, and in which Priestley
was said to be labouring in America 'to disunite the people
from their government, and to introduce the blessings of French
anarchy'.

By the middle of July 1798 the aliens and sedition Acts had
passed Congress, and it was not long before some of those who
were close to the President, especially Timothy Pickering,
Secretary of State, began to think of Priestley and Cooper as
men to whom the Acts might be applicable.[1] To allay such
suspicions, Priestley compiled and published in 1799 his *Letters
to the Inhabitants of Northumberland*, in which he again plainly
stated his opinion of the administration. Some of his friends
thought that he was wrong to justify himself in this way, and
that it would have been better to remain silent.

[1] See e.g. Priestley's letters to Thatcher (Thacher) in *Proc. Massachusetts Hist.
Soc.*, 1886–7, 3(2S), 11–40.

But privately he could not stay silent; in fact, he lost no opportunity to speak straightly to those in high places. Thus, writing to George Thatcher, Member of Congress from Maine, on 7 January 1799, he said: 'It is clear to me that you have violated your constitution in several essential articles, and act upon maxims by which you may defeat the whole object of it.' After all he had been through, he could not refrain from such comments. 'I am not used to secrecy or caution, and I cannot adopt a new system of conduct now.' Again on 8 February 1799, he wrote:

I am as busy in my way as you are in yours, and I hope to better purpose; for, in my opinion, you are doing a great deal of mischief, tho I doubt not with the best intentions.

He thanked Thatcher for copies of Adams's messages to Congress, but added that he thought they were very improper coming in the name either of the President or the Secretary of State. Only public papers relating to facts were ever laid before the House of Commons in England, without any reasoning that tended to prejudge the issue.

Neither your President, nor Secretary, write in a manner becoming their situation. Their charges against the French are probably very just; but the language in which they speak of them is not that of men who wish for peace. You will get into an open war, or worse, if you can. This, however, is the business of your statesmen; tho happily not of you only. You are but puppets in the hand of one whose wisdom makes use of your folly, and no doubt for the best purposes.

It was characteristic of Priestley that he saw nothing incongruous in following this broadside with a request that Thatcher would obtain for him a yard or two of oiled silk for some electrical experiments.

On 1 August 1799 Pickering decided to take action on a letter he had received from Charles Hall, Marshal of the Circuit Court, concerning an address by Cooper that he printed in his own paper on 29 June and that had been reprinted in the *Aurora* on 12 July. This contained a strong criticism of the government in general, and of Adams in particular. Pickering also had information that Priestley had attended a democratic celebration on 4 July, and had busied himself in distributing copies of Cooper's address in the form of handbills. Cooper, who had practised as a barrister in England, had taken the precaution of first becoming admitted to American citizenship. 'I am sorry for it,' Pickering wrote to Adams, 'for those who are desirous of maintaining our internal tranquillity must wish them both removed from the United States.'

On 13 August, Adams replied that he thought Cooper's address was a libel on the government and that he ought to be prosecuted. The idea of expelling Priestley, however, was unacceptable, though the reasons he gave were not complimentary. 'He is as weak as water, as unstable as Reuben, or the wind. His influence is not an atom in the world.'

On 26 October 1799 the *Reading Weekly Advertiser* pointed out that Cooper had formerly applied to the President for appointment as 'agent for settling the respective claims of the citizens of this country and Great-Britain' and that Priestley had supported him. The President had rejected the application with disdain, and Cooper's address was to be regarded as an act of revenge on the government. The paper did not explain how it had learnt the contents of what should have been a confidential letter from the President to the Secretary of State. Priestley's approach and his subsequent attitude to the government had certainly annoyed Adams, who afterwards said to Jefferson: 'I have great complaints against him for personal injuries and persecution, at the same time that I forgive all.'

Cooper immediately replied to the Reading paper, exonerating Priestley from any connection with the address. At the time of his application for the post, he said, Adams was 'hardly in the infancy of political mistake'. America was not then saddled with the expense of a standing army. Adams had not then projected his various foreign embassies, nor had he attempted to influence the decisions of a court of law.

Cooper, it seems, insisted on being a political martyr so as to show up the retrograde tendencies of the sedition Act, which was passed at a time when America was on the brink of declaring war on France. But there is no doubt also that Cooper's prosecution was a tactical error on the part of the government.

He was found guilty, and fined four hundred dollars with six months' imprisonment.

The trial began on 11 April 1800. Before judgment was finally passed on 30 April, the Reading paper had found another topic which suited its policy—a family scandal that proved the bitterest experience of Priestley's life. His son William was accused by the paper of having attempted, in the absence of his brother Joseph in England, to poison his father and the rest of the household, by adding arsenic to the meal chest. The anonymous correspondent said that there was nothing strange in this affair. Priestley and his son were full of French principles, and there had been many similar attacks on parents in France since the Revolution.

It was not until 7 June that a letter from William Priestley, who denied the allegation, and another to him from his father, appeared in the paper. By then William was at Middle Paxton, having left Northumberland with his family six days before the accident happened. Priestley said:

> I examined what remain'd of the flour, and cannot say that I found any appearance of Arsenic in it; and Dr. Cosins always said he was confident from what he observed of the operation of it, that there was nothing besides Tartar Emetic in what we had taken. Since therefore no real mischief has been done, and it cannot be proved that any was intended, I shall not make any further enquiry into the business . . .
>
> I am as ever, your affectionate father . . .

The *Reading Weekly Advertiser* was not convinced by this carefully worded letter that kept strictly to the truth, for the arsenic —if such it had been—was only visible in the top part of the meal (which had been thrown away) and not in what remained in the chest afterwards. The paper suggested that William should return to Northumberland and stand trial. Only in this way could his guilt or innocence be established. Naturally, he did not respond to the suggestion.

Copies of the statements by father and son were sent to England, in case the story should reach the papers there. Lindsey thought that William would have abhorred such an attempt on his father's life, but that his wife was not altogether free from suspicion. William, however, was heavily in debt, and had left to try to make good elsewhere. Priestley had undertaken to pay his debts and to make up the total to £1,300. 'For I must not wholly desert him,' he told Wilkinson, 'and indeed I feel more compassion than resentment on his account. He is gone to seek a settlement in the Western Territory, and I do not expect, or wish to see him any more; but I shall continue to write to him, and give him my best advice.'

William's departure and Cooper's imprisonment were not the only things that Priestley had on his mind. Writing to Wilkinson in June 1800, he referred to John Vaughan's business failure—a serious matter, as he held all Priestley's capital. That it should have occurred at a time when William's debts had to be met was particularly unfortunate, and he would probably have been in serious trouble had not gifts and legacies from old or deceased friends continued to arrive, thus confirming his belief in a beneficent Providence to the end of his days. Eventually Vaughan's assignees were prevailed upon to make Priestley an annual allowance of $500 for five years.

Throughout his life Priestley had found strength in adversity, and even now, when everything seemed against him, he was able to say that he had never been more successful in his pursuits than in recent months. He also saw hope on the political horizon, though he was still subject to public abuse. 'It is what every man who does any good in the world must expect, and is much more than balanced by the approbation of persons of similar sentiments and views; and of such cordial friends, I have never been destitute.'

One such friend was Jefferson himself, who was alert to the value for America of distinguished immigrants. In January 1800, he consulted both Priestley and E. I. du Pont de Nemours (who had recently arrived from France) in connection with a plan of long standing for the reform of the educational system of Virginia. He asked Priestley to help by recommending a course of instruction in the sciences, so that he could attract the best professors from Europe for his proposed new public institution of higher learning. Priestley gave thought to the matter and wrote his views in some 'Hints concerning Public Education' in May.

By the later months of 1800, as Adams's term was ending,

many thought that Jefferson would soon be returned as President. It was then that Priestley decided to make one final visit to Philadelphia to settle his affairs. He had intended to stay for a fortnight only, but he was taken seriously ill with fever, and for several weeks his friends despaired of his life. Somehow the rumour reached France that he was suffering from the after-effects of poisoning, and this, according to Cuvier, shortened his life. But the facts seem otherwise. He was attended by his friend Rush, who diagnosed the illness as 'a bilious fever with pleurisy'. Rush's treatment of him included seven profuse bleedings, and this in itself might explain why his recovery was protracted.

Jefferson took office on 4 March 1801, and shortly afterwards he learned that Priestley was still in Philadelphia. In spite of his many preoccupations, Jefferson found time to write him a charming and consoling letter.[1] 'Yours is one of the few lives precious to mankind,' he said, 'for the continuance of which every thinking man is solicitous.'

Our countrymen have recovered from the alarm into which art & industry had thrown them, science & honesty are replaced on their high ground, and you, my dear Sir, as their great apostle, are on its pinnacle. It is with heartfelt satisfaction that, in the first moments of my public action, I can hail you with welcome to our land, tender to you the homage of it's respect & esteem, cover you under the protection of those laws which were made for the wise & the good like you, and disdain the legitimacy of that libel on legislation which under the form of a law was for some time placed among them.

Nothing could have been more calculated to speed Priestley's recovery, and not long afterwards he was able to return to Northumberland and prosecute his scientific and literary work with renewed vigour. He resumed a controversy with men of science in the *Medical Repository* in Philadelphia,[2] still arguing in favour of phlogiston and aiming to point out that the anti-phlogistic theory of Lavoisier and his followers, by then almost universally accepted, was by no means perfect. But he was more interested in developments in Europe, which he read about

[1] Published first by Theophilus Lindsey. The original, now in the Library of Congress, was transcribed by D. McKie, *Notes & Records*, 1952, *10*, 55.

[2] See Sidney M. Edelstein, 'The Chemical Revolution in America . . .', *Chymia*, 1959, 5, 155 ff.

mainly in the *Philosophical Magazine* (started in 1798) and *Nicholson's Journal* (begun in 1802). There he saw that wonderful new developments were taking place at the hands of a new generation of men, most of whom could be ranked among the friends of liberty and of the Dissenters—men like Thomas Henry's son, William; John Dalton, also of Manchester; and Humphry Davy, who had corresponded with him after meeting Joseph junior at the Pneumatic Medical Institution at Clifton, where he had taken his sister, Sally, for consultations and treatment by Dr Beddoes. Priestley recognized a kindred spirit in Davy, and wrote to him saying that he regarded him as his true successor in pneumatic chemistry and that he felt able now to leave the development of the subject in Davy's hands.

Thus it was not merely chance that led Davy to combat the French views of chemical reactions and especially combustion phenomena, and to produce the experimental evidence that led to the downfall of the antiphlogistic theory. Nor was it merely coincidence that Henry's law of the solubility of gases and Dalton's law of partial pressures emerged from their study of Priestley's writings. Both of them, indeed, received much of their inspiration from Priestley. In his interpretation of diffusion, Dalton showed a knowledge of Priestley's various experiments on the generation of air from water, in part the subject of the last experimental paper he published (1793) before leaving England. Is it too much to expect that Dalton, like many other Dissenters, also read and was influenced by the preface to this work? Here he would have found a passage that may well have acted as a spur to many young men of his generation.

Since . . . the friends of philosophy in this country *must* separate on the ground of *religion* and *politics* . . . may the separation have no farther consequence than that of producing a generous emulation who shall most advance the cause of science; the friends of *church* and *king*, as they affect exclusively to call themselves, or the friends of *liberty*, among whom, at all times, and in all circumstances, I shall be proud to rank myself. We are, it is true, but a small minority, but not deficient, I trust, in ability, activity, and energy; qualities which will always make men respected, though oppressed.

Nor can we believe that Dalton, who introduced the atomic theory to help to explain the physical and chemical behaviour of gases, had failed to read the concluding paragraph of this publication, in which Priestley gave his final briefing, as it were, to the younger men he was leaving to carry on his work.

I cannot conclude this paper without observing that the advances we are continually making in the analysis of natural substances into the *elements* of which they consist, bring us but one step nearer to their constitutional differences; since as much depends upon their *mode of arrangement*, concerning which we know nothing at all, as upon the elements themselves. For things the most different in their properties appear to consist of the very same elements . . .

So much was common ground, though there was still no certainty as to which substances were elements and which had a compound nature. But now a new problem emerged.

By what means we can ever come at the knowledge of the internal arrangement of the elementary parts of natural substances, I have not the least idea. Notwithstanding this, the success with which our inquiries have hitherto been crowned should encourage us to despair of nothing. Nature exhibits an infinitely large field, but our powers of investigation seem also to increase without limits.

Before Priestley died, Dalton, in the autumn of 1803, had begun to make much progress in this new field of exploration and was able to give a preliminary account of his work to the Manchester Literary and Philosophical Society, and, on a visit to London as the guest of Davy, to those attending a course of lectures at the Royal Institution in the following January.

Priestley meanwhile, finding that his scientific acquaintances tired of the dispute over phlogiston, turned his thoughts to England and endeavoured to arouse interest there with notes in Nicholson's *Journal* 'On the Theory of Chemistry'. But this also proved unsatisfactory, owing largely to delays in communication. Thus he received the issue for May 1802 on 4 November that year, and though he replied on 5 November his rejoinder was not printed until February 1803. In the course of such exchanges, however, it became clear that what Priestley had earlier called combined fixed air (carbon monoxide) was in fact a new gas, and this, in the changed language of chemistry, became known as 'gaseous oxide of carbone' to distinguish it from fixed air (carbon dioxide), which was now called 'carbonic acid'.

Priestley also carried out some experiments on the Voltaic pile in 1801, using for this purpose an apparatus designed and presented to him by a young man of Birmingham, by name Weatherby Phipson. It consisted of 60 plates of copper coated with silver, and 60 thin-rolled plates of zinc. These experiments were published in Nicholson's *Journal* in March 1802. Priestley realized that his materials were not as reliable as those he had been used to obtaining in England, and that because of his isolation he was liable to be anticipated in his results. It pleased him that he was still listened to with respect, though none was prepared to consider a reintroduction of phlogistic ideas. Thus Bostock, reviewing Priestley's paper, made it clear that he was now out of the running in the rapid progress that was being made.

It contains a number of interesting experiments performed by this venerable philosopher, principally with a view to establishing his favourite hypothesis of phlogiston, to which he still adheres. Some of the facts which he notices had been previously observed in England, though from his remote situation he had not the opportunity of becoming acquainted with them.

Despite these handicaps, Priestley continued to carry out experiments and to send papers to the American Philosophical Society while his health remained, and his two last papers showed the same verve and originality that he had displayed in his earlier work.

Thus in the summer of 1803 he carried out further experiments on the growth of algae in order to disprove Erasmus Darwin's ideas on spontaneous generation as contained in his posthumous 'Temple of Nature'. That organized bodies could appear spontaneously from substances with no organization Priestley regarded as disproved by experiment. Nor could he accept the crude evolutionary concepts in Erasmus Darwin's writings. He thought it certain that plants and animals could only arise from a pre-existing germ of the same kind—plants from seeds and animals from sexual intercourse. Any other view was 'out of the course of nature' and atheistic. Darwin had

17

similar ideas to those of Ingenhousz (p. 131) and thought that
he had found additional arguments in Priestley's experiments
on the vegetable green matter. Priestley thereupon repeated his
earlier experiments (pp. 130–1) with some variations, and
showed that no green matter could be formed unless the water
offered some access, however slight, to the atmosphere. A film of
oil on the water was sufficient to prevent its appearance, but a
loose tin cover was not.

He pointed out that Girtanner, in the *Philosophical Magazine*
for May 1800, had laughed at him for believing that the seeds
or germs of algae, moulds, and microscopic animals existed in
the atmosphere and were invisibly small, for many thought it
more probable that moulds, in particular, had no parents and
originated spontaneously.

From his new experiments Priestley thought it was now
unquestionable that 'various animalcules, as well as the seeds
of various plants, invisible to us, *do* float in the atmosphere'. It
remained for Pasteur to demonstrate the truth of this view some
half a century later.

In his final paper, sent from Northumberland on 21 November 1803, Priestley gave an account of his 'discovery' that salt, if
frequently mixed with snow as a freezing mixture, contained a
detectable quantity of nitre, that is, that nitric acid had been
formed in the atmosphere and carried down in the snow. In
earlier experiments he and Cavendish had found that when
common air was sparked with inflammable air a certain amount
of nitric acid was produced, and he now attempted to explain
its occurrence in the snow as the result of electric discharges in
the atmosphere. Here again his ingenuity showed itself. Though
at ground level the different gases were perfectly mixed by
diffusion, it was not impossible that in the upper atmosphere
there might be more of the lighter gases, including hydrogen.
The conditions would then be right for the production of nitric
acid under electric discharge. It was unfortunate that these
results were incorrect.

After his illness in Philadelphia, Priestley realized that little
time remained to him, and he spent most of his last years in
completing and publishing religious works and pamphlets which
had been delayed for various reasons not unconnected with the

domestic and political upheavals around him. The chief of these works was his *General History of the Christian Church*, the first two volumes of which had been published in Birmingham in 1790. He completed it with four more volumes which were printed at Northumberland in 1802–3, and a second edition of the first two volumes came out there in 1803–4. His earlier religious works were now better known in America, for his *History of the Corruptions of Christianity* had been published in both Philadelphia and Boston in 1797. His lectures on history and general policy and some other educational works were likewise produced at Philadelphia in their first American edition in 1803. A number of minor booklets continued to come from his pen. His last major achievement was an *Index to the Bible*, which appeared in Philadelphia in 1804 and afterwards in several London editions.

After 1801 Priestley had become noticeably less robust, and he suffered from constant indigestion, being forced to live mainly on soft foods. So he carried on for nearly three years, enjoying his correspondence with Jefferson and other notable people in Philadelphia and England, the companionship of his young grandchildren, the society of his many acquaintances in the locality of Northumberland, and the visits of Cooper. Just as in Birmingham Priestley had often brought men of very different beliefs and outlook together in friendship around his own table, so in Northumberland he showed how neighbours should live together in harmony, whatever differences might tend to separate them. 'When I lived at Northumberland with Dr Priestley,' Cooper later wrote, 'a more social place could not well be imagined.'

In January 1804 the symptoms he attributed to indigestion became alarming and his weakness increased. But still he rose and shaved himself, and went to his laboratory daily. By the end of the month he was forced to desist, and at times he found even speech difficult. On Thursday, 2 February, he made the last laconic entry in his diary: 'Much worse: incapable of business: Mr. Kennedy came to receive instructions about printing, in case of my death.' On Friday he appeared better, being up for much of the day, reading and correcting proofs. On the Sunday evening he called his grandchildren to his bedside and spoke to each in turn. He then explained: 'I am going to sleep as well as you: for death is only a good long sound sleep in the grave, and we shall meet again.'

During parts of the week-end and early Monday morning he seemed perfectly composed and cheerful, and gave further instructions to Cooper and Joseph about three pamphlets that they had agreed to see through the press for him. On the morning of Monday, 6 February, he dictated his final corrections, and having had them read back to him, he said: 'That is right; I have now done.'

Some forty minutes later, at about 11 o'clock, the end came, but so quietly that neither Joseph nor Elizabeth, who were close at hand, noticed anything. He simply put his hand to his face, and breathed his last.

Davy, looking back on the most productive period of scientific inquiry in the eighteenth century, had no hesitation in placing Priestley with Black, Cavendish, and Scheele as the four greatest chemical discoverers of the age. Priestley, he said, began his career as a scientist without any general knowledge of chemistry and with very limited apparatus. His characteristics were ardent zeal and the most unwearied industry. He exposed all the substances he could procure to chemical agencies, and brought forward his results as they occurred, without attempting logical method or scientific arrangement. His hypotheses, Davy said, were usually founded upon a few loose analogies; but he changed them with facility; and being framed without much effort, they were relinquished with little regret. Priestley, he added, possessed both ingenuousness and the love of truth in the highest degree. His manipulations, though never very refined, were always simple, and often ingenious.

It is impossible to disagree with this assessment, for Priestley himself frequently admitted as much. Science was never for long allowed to take first place in his life, and we have seen why this was so. Yet, despite the features that some still regard as shortcomings in a man of science, we must agree with Davy's final appraisal: 'Chemistry owes to him some of her most important instruments of research, and many of her most useful combinations; and no single person ever discovered so many new and curious substances.'

Far more than any other writer of his period, Priestley had made men think for themselves. In 1813 Adams exclaimed to Jefferson: 'Oh! that Priestley could live again.' Nine years after his death, his influence was still felt by both of them. Adams referred to 'this great, this learned, indefatigable, most excellent and extraordinary man . . . Peace, rest, joy and glory to his soul! For I believe he had one, and one of the greatest . . .' Jefferson remembered Priestley, not only as a man of science and an educationist, but also as a theological writer. 'I have read his Corruptions of Christianity, and Early Opinions of Jesus, over and over again; and I rest on them . . . as the basis of my own faith. These writings have never been answered . . .' But for Adams they raised more difficulties than they resolved: 'I shall never send you all the questions that I would have put to Priestley, because they are innumerable . . .'

To many of his contemporaries Priestley had been a burning and a shining light. But perhaps his own estimate was more apposite. As a flaming meteor or comet he seared the eighteenth-century firmament, and perforce dwindled in brilliance as he passed into the distance. But after an interval he returned and lived again in the minds of another generation to produce profound social changes. Philip Harwood, commenting on Priestley's return to public notice after the Napoleonic wars, said in 1842 that many of the most powerful influences that had contributed to the freer England of that time could be traced, 'by a spiritual genealogy of not more than two or three descents', to the great Heresiarch. Priestley again receded, but historians are now finding in his writings and thought a more lasting influence than had previously been realized. Some of his visions, left for the contemplation of future ages, have become accomplished fact within living memory. This is one peculiar aspect of Priestley's greatness. He belongs not only to England and the eighteenth century, but to the world and the generations yet to come who will respond fearlessly to the promptings of reason and conscience.

Bibliography and Sources

EXTENSIVE collections of the published works of Priestley and his close contemporaries are to be found in many centres, particularly in Dr Williams's Library, London, The British Museum, and the Birmingham Reference Library. Several foreign editions of Priestley's scientific writings can be seen at the Wellcome Historical Medical Library.

Manuscript source materials are widely scattered, mainly in England and America. The chief collection, including correspondence of Priestley, Lindsey, and their intimate friends, is in Dr Williams's Library. The Royal Society has material in the Canton Papers and the Priestley Memorial Volume (James Yates), and letters from Priestley to his sister Martha, James Lind, and especially Josiah and Tom Wedgwood. Priestley's correspondence with Richard Price (mostly published) has been preserved in the Bodleian Library, Oxford; a few letters (published) are in the Cambridge University Library, and still others in the Wellcome Historical Medical Library and in Birmingham (Reference Library and Assay Master's Office). The British Museum has material relating to the Priestley pedigree, notes between Priestley and John Wilkes and Edward Gibbon, and letters from or to Thomas Birch, Jeremy Bentham, J. H. Magellan, Arthur Young, and William Eden, as well as a large collection of public satirical prints depicting Priestley and his colleagues. Papers relating to the Birmingham Riots of 1791 and their aftermath can be consulted at the Warwickshire Records Office. Documents concerning the Warrington Academy are available (in microfilm) from the Warrington Public Library, which also has correspondence between Priestley and the Wilkinson brothers (copies elsewhere, e.g. British Museum and Birmingham Reference Library).

A file of *The Times* (in microfilm) can be consulted most conveniently at the Westminster Public Reference Library and Aris's *Birmingham Gazette* in the Birmingham Reference Library. Copies of the American papers mentioned are difficult to find, and I am grateful to the Historical Society of Berks. County, Reading, Pa., for photocopies of certain issues of the *Reading Weekly Advertiser*, and to the Historical Society of Pennsylvania, Philadelphia, for articles from the *Aurora*. The letter to Senator Thatcher (p. 238) was kindly transcribed by the former owner, Mr Raymond Szymanowitz of Springfield, New Jersey (original now in the Library of the Chemists' Club, New York).

The main work of reference on Priestley's life, correspondence, and non-scientific works is J. T. Rutt, *The Theological and Miscellaneous Works* . . ., London, 1817–32, 25 vols. in 26 pts., of which vol. 1 contains Memoirs and Correspondence, 1733–87, and Life and Correspondence, 1787–1804. Of the shorter accounts, only two can be called biographies, namely T. E. Thorpe, *Joseph Priestley*, London and New York, 1906, and Anne D. Holt, *A Life of Joseph Priestley*, London, 1931. Neither does full justice to all aspects of his work, and the lack of a standard biography is much to be regretted.

The best general account of Priestley's chemical work is to be found in J. R. Partington, *A History of Chemistry*, vol. III, 1962 (London: Macmillan; New York: St Martin's Press). It gives a very full list of other works to which reference may be made. Other reading lists of works dealing with Priestley and his contemporaries are given in J. G. Crowther, *Scientists of the Industrial Revolution*, 1962 (London: The Cresset Press). In addition, the student will find much of interest that helps to illustrate the many facets of the Priestley story in the following books, among others: Herschel C. Baker, *William Hazlitt*, 1962 (Cambridge, Mass.: Belknap Press; London: O.U.P.); Raymond G. Cowherd *The Politics of English Dissent* . . ., 1956 (New York: University Press); Elizabeth M. Geffen, *Philadelphia Unitarianism, 1796–1861*, 1961 (Philadelphia: University Press); William Turner (1761–1859), *The Warrington Academy*, reprinted 1957 (Warrington: Library and Museum Committee); and several works of H. McLachlan, especially *Letters of Theophilus Lindsey*, 1920;

English Education under the Test Acts, 1931; *The Religious Opinions of Milton, Locke and Newton*, 1941; *Warrington Academy: Its History and Influence*, 1943.

Finally, references to less familiar sources are given in the footnotes.

Index